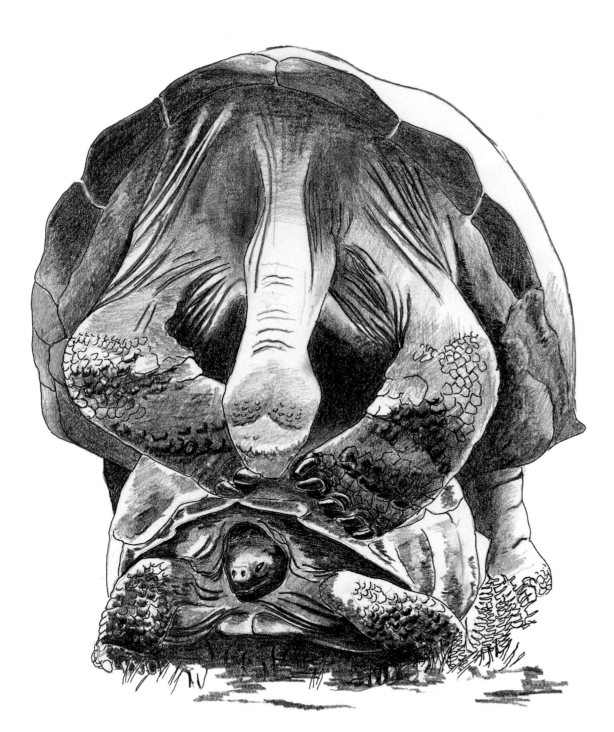

Tortoise mating on the Volcano Alcedo.
Reproductive success and the survival of the young to sexual
maturity are the keys to Restoring the Tortoise Dynasty.

RESTORING THE TORTOISE DYNASTY

By Godfrey Merlen

THE DECLINE AND RECOVERY OF THE GALAPAGOS GIANT TORTOISE

A PUBLICATION OF THE CHARLES DARWIN FOUNDATION - 1999

RESTORING THE TORTOISE DYNASTY

Sponsored by: Dennis Curry Charitable Trust.
                 Galapagos Conservation Trust.

Frankfurt Zoological Society.

Published by:
The Charles Darwin Foundation for the Galapagos Islands.
Casilla 17-01-3891 - Quito, Ecuador.

Printed by:
Imprenta Mariscal
Avenida 6 de diciembre 7015 e Isla Isabela - Quito, Ecuador.

Text, drawings and most photographs by Godfrey Merlen.
We appreciate the use of the following photographs.
Page 6 - Rollo Beck. Archives of the California Academy of Sciences.
Page 21 - Ole Hamann.
Page 41 - Parque Nacional Galápagos.
The drawing on page 1 is after a photograph by W.H. Tripp in 1914.
The drawing on pages 2, 14 and 44 are after photographs by C. MacFarland.
The drawing on page 4 is after a photograph be R. Perry.

Design by Godfrey Merlen and Juan Carlos Alvarado Ch.
Technical layout by Juan Carlos Alvarado Ch.

APPRECIATION AND DEDICATION

Restoring the Tortoise Dynasty is both a dedication and an appreciation. It is a dedication to the vision of the founders of the Charles Darwin Foundation, who believed in the possibility of saving the unique nature of the Galapagos Islands through scientific study and the application of knowledge.

Sadly, it was already known that the giant tortoises had been slaughtered in the thousands and that these animals represented an important element in the ecosystems of the islands where they lived. If the fauna and flora was to be preserved, then the extant tortoise populations, some of them almost annihilated, had to be given immediate assistance.

With very little to go on, and considerable doubt in the outside world that it was indeed possible to save the tortoises, the early directors of the Darwin Station doggedly worked in the untried field of breeding them in the environment of the embryonic,and financially poor, research station. They were assisted by the early park wardens, who also shared the dream of seeing the islands restocked by the magnificent reptiles. Time has rewarded their efforts and a large number of repatriated tortoises are starting to fill the panorama on some of the islands where populations were on the edge of extinction. The impetus of the early workers has been carried on into the present day by an equally dedicated group of people from both the Research Station and the National Park Service.

A large portion of the information in this book has not only been extracted from the library resource of the Research Station, well organized by Gayle Davis-Merlen, but also extracted from the records held by the Area of Protection under the leadership of Howard Snell. He replaced Linda Cayot, whose love of the great reptiles influenced all around her. But as much as these sources helped research the subject, the information lodged in the heads of people from both institutions was just as important. Cruz Márquez, herpetologist at the Station, was a mine of information, having tramped over many of the islands in search of elusive tortoises. So also was Fausto Llerena of the Park Service, who manages the practical side of raising the tortoises. Over the years has nurtured thousands of baby tortoises through their young years. His keen eye not only spots cryptic tortoise nests on remote islands, but also allows him to carve beautiful wooden tortoises that grace the houses of many people. In June 1999, he will be honored by naming the Breeding Center after him. Wacho Tapia is Head Officer and in charge of conservation programs run by the Park Service. He represents the new generation of managers - practical, intelligent, and tough - and was another well of information. I also enjoyed the untiring humor and the enthusiastic rough and tough lives of the park wardens, without whom all the conservation programs of the Galapagos would be of little count. Wiry, with excellent sense of direction, they are the rugged, rough Galapagos environment personified.

Four visiting scientists, all specialists in reptiles, gave freely of their knowledge. Joseph Flanagan, Elliott Jacobsen, James Gibbs and Jeff Powell.

It was the present Director of the Station, Dr. Robert Bensted-Smith who originated this project, which plunged me into the world of the giant tortoise, and I am extremely grateful for that experience.

I appreciated the enthusiasm of Eliecer Cruz, Director of the Galapagos National Park Service, in allowing me to accompany his fleet - footed wardens into the depths of Española Island to release the young tortoises.

Finally I think it is the lesson learned from the continuing success of the tortoise breeding program, largely based on a strong cooperation between the Research Station and the Park Service, that should be a guiding light onto the future conservation efforts of the Galapagos Islands. Dedication and a vision can overcome all obstacles.

Godfrey Merlen.
Puerto Ayora, Santa Cruz, Galapagos. April 1999

INTRODUCTION

The arrival of ships, which brought introduced animals and hungry men, had a devastating effect on the giant tortoises of Galapagos.

Isles of the Tortoises

No more fitting a description could be found for the Galapagos Islands. Remote in the expanses of the eastern Pacific Ocean, the archipelago remained a lost world where reptiles had become a dominant feature in the wild volcanic landscape.

Fiery-colored iguanas, in their coats of golds and reds, paced the heights of the great volcanoes, seeming a reflection of the molten lavas that frequently fountained from the dark slopes. On the coast, the black marine iguanas, as dark as the lava fields they lived and bred upon, plunged into the cold upwellings to search out their sustenance, the green fronds of rapidly growing seaweeds. Between the coast and the cloud-covered heights, the land was a haven for the fleet-footed lava lizards and their predators, the dark snakes with their golden bands or stripes.

But, above all, there was nothing to compare with the giant tortoises. Nothing could startle the eye nor catch the imagination more than the sight of thousands of these monstrous reptiles grazing in the pastures of the volcanoes. Their dark, almost black bodies moved hither and thither, reflecting the sun like water or glistening when wetted by the mists which swept through the orchid and moss — laden trees. Their colonization of the islands had been extremely successful. They not only succeeded in establishing themselves on dry, low islands, but on high moist ones as well. Tough as the land they lived upon, their scaly feet withstood the harsh, rocky ground. Strong, curved, knife-like mouths allowed them to feed upon the spiny cactus and acacias when all other vegetation was dry and leafless through the lack of rain. Above all, their slow metabolic rate permitted them to beat the droughts which periodically smote the Archipelago. Living at a low ebb in the shade of caves and rocky crevices, they remained like stones through months of blasting heat, when the soil turned to dust. When the rains finally came, the great animals eased out of their slumbers and rocky recesses and lumbered off to feast in a fresh and vitalized world, now leafy and green. Pools of water, caught in the baked land or on the sculptured rocks, awaited them. And they slaked their thirst by the gallon!

On some islands the creatures made extensive migrations, many kilometers in length. They moved from nesting areas, where the temperature and the moisture in the soil were suitable to their reproductive needs, to regions where food and water were more abundant. These journeys often extended from the sunny coast to the gloomy highlands.

It was a quiet world, broken only by the scraping of shell against rock, the hiss of a quickly retracted head, or the low, rhythmic, grunting bellow of the mating male. Predators did not exist for such large reptiles, but the hatchlings were taken by the native hawks and quite possibly by the endemic rice rats, some species of which are now extinct. Yet the world was in a certain balance, for the reproductive capacity of the tortoises was such that they survived this loss of their young. Thus the hawks survived, the tortoises survived, and the vegetation survived at a more or less stable level.

How many tortoises were there? No one knows, yet there is no doubt that there were many thousands - even hundreds of thousands. Some say a million.

Why don't we know? Well, the situation changed. Changed so drastically that we will never know the answer - at least not in *our* generation. It was the inevitable arrival of mankind that caused the dramatic decline in numbers. So severe was the effect that some populations have become extinct. Yet, at a later date, it was the dedication of that same species, man, that has given us the visionary hope that all is not lost. That one day the giant tortoises will live as they did before the catastrophe. The essence of that hope is a program that was started shortly after the Charles Darwin Foundation was created in 1959 and authorized by the Ecuadorian government to undertake conservation work in the Galapagos. It was the investigation of the biology of the giant tortoise and the first tentative steps at breeding them and hatching their eggs in captivity that encouraged the program's growth and enormous success. As of January 1999, there has been a total of *two thousand four hundred and ninety - four* reared tortoises, from eight different populations, returned to the wild. That is an average of seventy - five per year. Today the Tortoise Breeding Program is run by a dedicated National Park Service with technical input from the Charles Darwin Research Station. It has become a symbol of conservation effort in the islands. The isles of the tortoises will not be a hazy memory but a reality.

THE UNCONSCIOUS YEARS

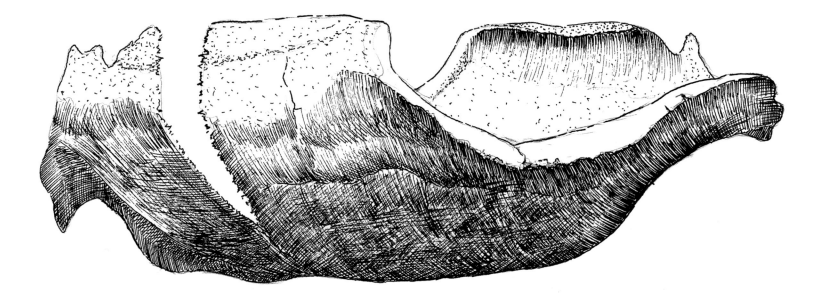

The shell of a giant tortoise (killed by machete) from the island of Pinta. 1971.

From the first time that a human being stepped on the shores of Galapagos in 1535, the giant tortoise was an outstanding feature of the landscape. Unfortunately the eye was not the only human sensibility to feast upon this extraordinary sight. Hunger was but one pace behind. It was soon discovered that the flesh of the tortoise was excellent eating. Moreover, the slow-moving animals could neither escape, nor were they aggressive. When frightened, they merely dropped to the ground, retracting their heads within the tough shells, and slamming the front door by bringing the front legs in as far as possible. This served them little in the face of the keen-bladed machete, which opened them from end to end with a few quick blows. Also, in a land where water was at a premium, the human voyagers found another attraction. The tortoise contained his own water tanks - the bladder and the pericardium (the sack around the heart). These liquids the hunter found as sweet as water.

The destruction had a slow beginning, as few people could even find the "enchanted islands" and, when they did, the harsh land was not welcoming. One hundred and fifty years after the discovery of the islands, they became a hangout for pirates and buccaneers. One of them, Ambrose Cowley, summed up the fact that fated the land turtle.

"Guanas are as plenty there as in any place of the world and extraordinary *sweet meate* but the Land Turtle as they exceed in sweetness soe doe they in like manner in numbers for it is incredible to report how numerous they are and I believe there is not any place in the world that have such plenty of these Creatures." This was in 1684.

Even so the affair might not have become totally out of hand had not the lure of untapped whaling grounds brought the fleets from the Atlantic, particularly the New England states. In 1789 the *Amelia*, sailing out of London, was the first whaling vessel to double the Horn and penetrate the Pacific Ocean. She was also the first ship to take sperm whales off the South American coast The scarcity of whales in the Atlantic and the exciting early results of the first boats caused an avalanche of economic adventurers to send their vessels westward. By the 1840s, 600 boats had entered the Pacific. The numbers peaked around 1846 with some 735 ships. In thirty-five years the fleet removed about four and a half million gallons of sperm oil. Seven hundred and thirty - five ships! And how many bellies to fill! Voyages lasted several years and fresh food was always at a premium. Within a few short decades, the giant tortoise populations declined faster than that of the sperm whale. The Galapagos was not only a whaling area in itself — and still to this day a lucky observer may see sperm whales in the waters bathing the massive shield volcanoes — but the islands became well known as a source of meat for all the boats heading westward to the deep - water offshore whaling grounds and those of Japan.

The whaling bark *Morning Star*.

Apart from its good - tasting flesh, another facet of the tortoise exacerbated their decline. Stacked up in the hold or penned on the deck, they lived for months on end with no food or water. One that was lost on the whaler *Niger* is said to have been found alive amongst some casks after two years!

The job of collecting fell to the whole crew, who went ashore in droves to search for the tortoises. It was called "turpining," since the animals were called "turpins," and most of them were brought to the shore on the backs of men. This technique was termed "backing them down." Once a man was in tortoise country, it may not have been too difficult to move about, for the tortoises in their ambling over the millennia had created veritable roadways, often giving access to the steepest slopes and through the densest vegetation. But getting there, and back with a load, was another thing, for the heat was tremendous and the terrain often difficult. It was for this reason that the whalers preferred animals that weighed between fifty and seventy-five pounds. That meant females and juveniles. This bias jeopardized the chances of the reproduction and recruitment to the adult populations, further aiding their rapid decline. Bigger tortoises were taken, too. Lashed to oars or stout posts, they were hauled away to the shore on the shoulders of two men.

Thus it continued year after year, decade after decade. An endless conveyer belt destroying a unique resource and few voices heard in its defense! Not just a few animals, not even tens, but hundreds and hundreds, thousands and thousands.

Individual "turpining" trips were incredibly profitable to men starved of fresh meat:

> In 1831 the ship *Isabel* took 335 from Isabela.
> In 1834 the ship *Moss* took 350 from Floreana.
> In 1837 the ship *Onega* took 240 from San Cristobal.

The tortoises were known to have been taken from nine islands: Española, Floreana, Isabela, Pinta, Pinzon, San Cristobal, Santa Cruz, Santa Fe, Santiago.

Of course it couldn't last. In the 1830s tortoises vanished from Floreana. Later they were extirpated from Santa Fe (although some modern researchers doubt

Sailor "backing down" a living tortoise.

the existence of this race, believing the tortoises to have been dumped there by tortoise gatherers who obtained them from another island). In 1848 the whaler *Good Return* reported no tortoises on Santiago, where fourteen tons had been collected in 1813 by one vessel.

Charles Townsend, Director of the New York Aquarium in 1925, made an extensive study of the extant logbooks of the whalers. From these it is known that over 13,000 tortoises were removed. This figure is very incomplete, as it represents seventy-nine vessels that made one hundred and eighty-nine visits from 1831 to 1868. Extrapolating such numbers to the whole fleet may indicate that well over 100,000 tortoises were taken by all the boats in the same time span. By the 1860s the number of tortoises taken was probably halved, but by then the whale stocks were also greatly reduced. The discovery of large quantities of petroleum in 1859 rapidly led to the replacement of whale oil lights by those utilizing kerosene. This situation might have resulted in a breathing space for the surviving tortoises. The difficulty of removing the remaining heavy reptiles from the interior was protecting them. But it was not to be.

By the 1830s people were already living permanently on the islands. The colonists on Floreana soon learned that there was a good trade to be made in tortoises. This perhaps was the final blow to the population there. But this did not stem the tide, for soon trips were organized from Floreana to Santa Cruz and Santiago in search of the valuable animals. Charles Darwin spent a while at a tortoise hunting camp on Santiago in 1835. In time people became aware of places deep within the interior where tortoises could still be found. However, whilst these forays were taking place, the colonists brought another invasion with them: their domestic animals and the rats of Europe.

Adult giant tortoises have no natural enemies. Even in the face of man, their passive defense was their large size and ponderous weight — they can easily top 150 kilos. The difficulty of the terrain, the lack of roads, the spiny vegetation, and the long distances all made their removal

Typical method of bringing out heavy tortoises from the hinterland.

difficult. However, there are delicate moments in the world of the tortoise which are independent of size and weight. In order to reproduce, the females search out the few areas where soil, temperature, and moisture all come together to provide a suitable environment for the construction of nests and the incubation of the hard-shelled, almost round, white eggs. A female constructs her nest with the back legs, forming a hole about 35 to 40 cm deep, slightly wider at the bottom than the top. You might think that the eggs would be damaged by their fall into the hole, but no. They are lowered down on strings of thick, transparent mucus, which helps them defy gravity to give them a soft landing. After burying the eggs and patting down the soil with the underside of her shell (the plastron) and the tops of her feet, the female wanders off leaving the eggs and the eventual hatchlings to nature's care - a system that had worked extremely well for millennia. But a new devastating change was now taking place. Pigs were one of the domestic stock introduced as food by the colonists.

Eventually they escaped from the confines of their human owners. With an acute sense of smell and equipped with sharp teeth, the free-roaming, intelligent animals soon located the sites of the beach-nesting marine turtles and those of the tortoise. Tearing apart the shallow nests gave them quick access to this protein-rich dinner. Thousands of nests were destroyed in this way, seriously compromising the tortoises' ability to rebuild their populations after the severe depletions caused by the whalers. Dogs soon learned the same trick. Donkeys and cattle also began to wander widely over the Galapagos landscape and also contributed to the decline of the tortoises, for they frequented the same trails made by the reptiles. The high pressure of their heavy weight upon relatively small feet was sufficient to damage the eggs in the soil beneath. The nesting areas were also popular with the donkeys, for they were relatively free of rocks and were excellent places for a good roll.

So, pigs, dogs, donkeys, and cattle. What else?

One animal that was not brought willingly to the islands, but which has accompanied western man wherever he has gone, was the black rat of Europe. Over time they were introduced accidentally onto many of the islands. Although the rats were apparently not particularly interested in the eggs of the tortoises, even if they could get at them in the nests, the tiny, soft-shelled hatchlings were at grave risk. Rats, with their sharp incisors, have no difficulty in gnawing into them, an easy meal in a harsh environment. On the island of Pinzon, there is good evidence that there has been no successful hatchling survival *during the 20th century*, from this cause.

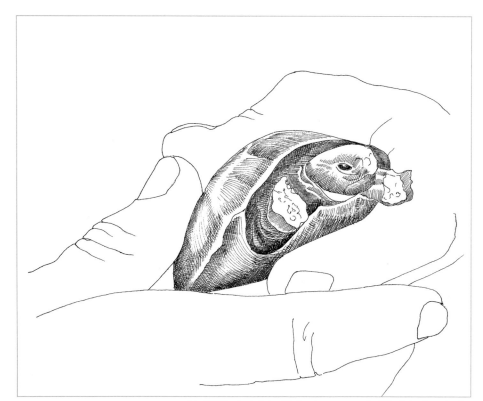

A hatchling tortoise with forelegs gnawed off by introduced rats.

Any more problems?

Yes. The goat was introduced. It is not a predator but a devastating competitor and causes serious changes in the environment. The climate of the Galapagos is excellent for these fast-breeding, herbivorous mammals, and their numbers soared. Fast and active, they outmaneuver the tortoise at every turn in the competition for vegetable resources. The land was soon denuded opening the soil to high solar radiation, erosion increased, and plant species began to disappear. The alteration of habitat may allow greater predation of the hatchling tortoises by hawks. The hot ground may inhibit the successful incubation of the eggs. On the island of Pinta, where the population of tortoises was greatly depleted by whalers, one male and two female goats were introduced in 1959. In ten years, the population had reached 3-5,000 and areas which had been covered by dense undergrowth now looked as bald as English parkland. In the early to mid 1970s the Research Station and the Park Service were able to devote more attention to the island and 25,000 goats were removed in twelve months. Forty thousand were removed before they were virtually eliminated. By then one tortoise, Lonesome George, survived. Twenty - eight skeletons were found in deep fissures toward the center of the island. Although they fell into the cracks as natural traps — perhaps covered by concealing ground cover — it is also possible that the tortoises, desperate in the face of a dwindling food supply, recklessly pushed on into areas that were lethal for them.

Could anything else conceivably go wrong?

In the swirling mists of Alcedo, goats strip out
the vegetation under the gaze of an old tortoise.
Erosion and habitat change are two major effects
of the introduced mammalian herbivores.

(5)

THE DESPAIRING YEARS

1901. Slaughter of tortoises for oil on Villamil Mountain (volcano Sierra Negra on southern Isabela).

*T*oward the end of the last century, scientific interest in the islands steadily grew. It had been known for many decades that the giant tortoises not only represented a rare and disappearing species, but also that they were curious in that they appeared different on the various islands. This seemed to suggest some sort of evolutionary process was at work. In many respects the process appeared to be similar to that which had modified the beak of the Darwin's Finches.

With the chaos left in the wake of the whaling fleet and the continuing and increased effect of the introduced animals, coupled to the rise in the human population, which was still killing tortoises, there grew a mounting concern that science would lose an unique tool to study evolution, should the tortoises go extinct. The result of this was a new invasion into the islands by a different breed of humans, the scientific collectors. Between them, they removed over 650 tortoises between 1888 and 1930. Although this number pales into insignificance compared to the early days of tortoise exploitation, it came at a time when the remaining animals could ill afford to lose a single individual. Yet the scientist believed that the giant reptiles were fated anyway and that they would disappear, leaving no material witness of their past presence.

In 1888 Edmund Heller, collecting for Stanford University, stated that authentic collections had been made from Tagus Cove and Iguana Cove on Isabela, Pinta, and Pinzon, " . . . the tortoises having become extinct on all the other islands of the archipelago." That would mean eleven species gone!

Frank Webster, who had handled about 125 specimens, remarked, " I consider now that these creatures are so nearly extinct that any remaining ones will be only stragglers, and will only be secured at a great expense of time, hardship, and money."

In 1900 Captain Noyes, on the *Julia E. Whalen*, the last recorded sealing vessel to visit the islands, searched Pinzon and found only four tortoises.

The year 1901 saw the arrival of Rollo Beck, an extremely dedicated scientific collector and observer, working from the small schooner, the *Mary Sachs*. He worked on the south side of the volcano Sierra Negra, then called Villamil Mountain, where people had been living for several years. Dogs were abundant and he was told that they snapped up every tortoise that hatched. Furthermore he found that hunters were busy working for a company on the mainland of Ecuador. Their product? Tortoise oil. Around two highland ponds Beck saw the grim remains of their work. Two hundred and fifty large animals, sacrificed for a gallon or two of oil from each. Other ponds nearby revealed the same dismal story of mayhem, but on a smaller scale. It was all too easy. Wait by the water and the animals will come to you. On the beach were twelve hundred gallons of oil ready for dispatch. This represented a minimum of 400 and a maximum of 1200 tortoises! Perhaps the scientists were not so far wrong in their pessimism for the survival of the reptiles!

In 1905 Beck came back, this time working for the California Academy of Sciences. This expedition was directed to document the biology of the islands, especially the tortoises. Several consequences of this major, year-long undertaking were of great importance. In the first place, a study collection of 256 tortoises was taken from populations all over the Archipelago. Not only was the reproductive state of the females noted but the collection became the first detailed study of shell morphology and taxonomy. The tough collector and his assistants explored deeply into many of the islands and were able to demonstrate that some of the populations that were considered extinct in fact survived. Meticulous notes were kept on locations, nests found, and many other details. At the end of the expedition, the following statement of abundance and scientific identification was made. It was an excellent basis for future work and gave a time perspective to future studies. The estimated 1974 abundance is indicated as well for comparison.

		1906		1974
	ISLAND	ABUNDANCE	NAME	ABUNDANCE
1.	Pinta	Rare	*abingdoni*	Very small
2.	Santiago	Rare	*darwini*	500-700
3.	Rabida	Very rare	*wallacei*	None
4.	Pinzon	Fairly abundant	*ephippium*	150-200
5.	Santa Cruz	Not rare	*porteri*	2000-3000
6.	Santa Fe	**EXTINCT**	?	**EXTINCT**
7.	San Cristobal	Nearly extinct	*chatamensis*	**500-700**
8.	Española	Very rare	*hoodensis*	20-30
9.	Floreana	**EXTINCT**	*elephantopus*	**EXTINCT**
10.	Fernandina	Very rare	*phantastica*	**EXTINCT**
11.	Villamil (Sierra Negra, Isabela)	Abundant	*güntheri*	200-300 (south and east) / 100-200 (west)
12.	Iguana Cove (Cerro Azul, Isabela)	Fairly numerous	*vicini*	400-600
13.	Tagus Cove (Darwin Volcano, Isabela)	Fairly numerous	*microphyes*	1000-2000
14.	Bank's Bay (Wolf Volcano, Isabela)	Fairly numerous	*becki*	1000-2000
15.	Cowley Mountain (Alcedo Volcano, Isabela)	Rare	*vandenburghi*	3000-5000

The 1974 figures give a maximum of 13,870 and a minimum of 8,420. This rather large difference is because the tortoises are often very difficult to count and much difficult terrain has never been visited.

One of the immediate conclusions is that of the fifteen proposed "species," three are extinct. The one specimen from Rabida is now generally considered to have been introduced to that island. Thus eleven remain.

The work carried out by Beck was very thorough. As can be seen from the table above, the expedition discovered all the extant populations known today, although it did not define the exceptional size of the one on Cowley Mountain (Alcedo), since Beck collected only one example. Moreover, the discovery of the remains of fourteen tortoises on Santa Fe established the previously suspected existence of this population as a strong probability.

Although the "discovery" of populations that were thought extinct was encouraging, the notes of the expedition constantly refer to the problems of the introduced animals and the spreading of the human population, which was still killing tortoises. An edition of the herpetological field notes of Joseph Slevin, edited by Thomas and Pat Fritts, is titled "Race with Extinction" and sums up well the feeling of the times.

In 1925, Charles Townsend, Director of the New York Aquarium, published " The Galapagos Tortoise in their relation to the whaling industry." His concluding remark was infinitely depressing: ". . . if the islands could be cleared of the pests introduced by civilized man and the original conditions restored! This is now impossible on the Galapagos. The only remaining hope for the race is the establishment of survivors elsewhere."

Townsend's recommendation was taken up in 1928 by the New York Zoological Society. An expedition was mounted, which resulted in the last major collection to be made - 180 living tortoises were taken from southern Isabela and distributed across the United States, from the zoo in Honolulu to the aquarium in New Orleans. They were also sent to Bermuda, Panama, and finally to Sydney, Australia. Were these to be the last remnants of the giant tortoises that roamed the Galapagos in their thousands? The history of many of these animals is now misty and unclear but in general the tortoises survived and a number still live today. The reproduction in captivity was dismally poor, yet it did show that breeding was possible. The tortoises that were sent to the San Diego Zoo have a more detailed history. One of them was finally returned in 1977 to play a vital part in the saving of the Española race.

But even as late as 1967 the depression concerning the fate of the animals had not lifted. The apparent lack of reproductive success in captive animals led to the suggestion that possibly the long - living tortoises, isolated on the islands for eons with few predators and abundant food, before the arrival of the goats and other herbivores, were now incapable of rapid reproduction, even that reproduction might be relatively uncommon. Thus any breeding program might at best be a hit and miss affair with little chance except of random success.

Reproduction is possible!

After the late 1920s, through the troubled times of the Second World War, and into the 1950s, little is reported from the islands as regards the tortoises. But in the mid-fifties the biologist Iraenus Eibl-Eibesfeldt visited the islands and returned home in a state of alarm about the ecological condition of the Archipelago. This started an international movement of conservationists, and scientists which culminated, in 1959 (the centenary of the publication of Darwin's *On the Origin of Species*), with the creation, in Belgium, of the Charles Darwin Foundation for the Galapagos Islands. The Foundation was not the object in itself but was the tool by which a biological research station would be set up, which, in turn, would have a practical function in the conservation of the islands. With the first President of the Charles Darwin Foundation, Victor Van Straelen, who had done so much for conservation in Africa, and the invaluable help of the Ecuadorian ambassador in Paris, Cristóbal Bonifaz, the government of Ecuador authorized the Foundation to set up the sorely needed Research Station. In the first article of the agreement between the Foundation and the government of Ecuador, it was understood that scientists should study the islands and the surrounding seas from any aspect which would help to conserve the unique and remarkable flora and fauna in their natural environments. And not a moment too soon! For although in that same year the San Diego Zoo reported the first birth of giant tortoises - hatched in a concrete crock in the reptile house - in the thirty-one years that Galapagos tortoises had lived in the zoo, the same article announced that they were extinct on eight of the islands where they once lived! What had happened since the California Academy's estimates from their expedition of 1906? Had so many died or been killed that five *more* island populations had disappeared in fifty-three years?

The Charles Darwin Research Station was inaugurated in 1964. Although the early history is now growing a little difficult to read on the ageing yellow archived pages, there can be no question of the dedication of the early employees and their belief in the Foundation's vision that there had to be a better future for these unique islands than the gloom expressed in the outside world.

Even before the Research Station's inauguration, the Research Station's first conservation officer, Miguel Castro, was out in the field searching for the beleaguered tortoises, trudging over the lava fields, bursting through the spiny vegetation, thirsty, hot, and tired. It was, in a sense, a search for the Holy Grail, for the tortoise is the very symbol of Galapagos and its conservation. Without them, what was there to hang on to? After all, the very name Galapagos had its origin in the shape of the tortoise shell that so reminded the early Spanish travelers of *galapago*, a horse saddle with a high pommel, that they were named for it.

Throughout the 1960s the records are full of expeditions to Española, to San Cristobal, to Isabela, Marchena, Pinta, Pinzon, and down into the forests of Santa Cruz, on which island the Research Station was situated.

By the mid 1960s the status of the tortoise populations was becoming clear.

- A tiny group of dispersed adult animals on Española, but no young.

- Pinzon with an aging population of adults, but no young.

- Pinta. Nothing, even after a map had become criss-crossed by the trails of the early, tough field workers. But goats. Yes. By the thousand. And the vegetation reduced to wreckage.

- South Isabela. The oil hunters had gone, but only just. The people from Beck's time were long absent, but in 1946 a penal colony was operated in the same region and the prisoners were sent out to bring in oil once more. Forty to one hundred gallons (say 20-50 tortoises) had been exported every month or so. By a local account, seven hundred were killed. The prisoners at Alemania, a remote region in the saddle between the two massive volcanoes of Cerro Azul and Sierra Negra, had eaten the reptiles to survive. The populations were now scattered and small. Rollo Beck had described them as abundant. No more.

- On San Cristobal the results were a little brighter. A population came to light on the north end of the island. Slow work but rewarding. Four adults were found in 1965. Eight in 1967. Fifty-seven in 1969.

The best news was the discovery of the very large population on Alcedo - previously known as Cowley Mountain. John Van Denburgh, herpetologist at the California Academy of Sciences, described the species as rare, since only one specimen was found on the slopes of the volcano in 1906. On the first research trip in 1963, no tortoises were found, yet, temptingly, a number of recent scats were located. A year later sightings from a helicopter used by members of the Galapagos International Scientific Project — a project which was influential in reinforcing the legal strength and powers of the Station — indicated that tortoises *were* there, right inside the caldera. In March of 1965 the climber Eric Shipton visited the Archipelago and was asked by the Station director to keep an eye open for tortoises on Alcedo. He counted seventy-nine! Hot foot after this exciting news, an extensive walk took Miguel Castro to the floor of the huge caldera. Caught in the rough lava at night, plagued by ticks, and severely short of water, he pushed on to finally find and mark 179 individuals of the magnificent Alcedo population. He investigated the lake of the powerful geyser, finding that the temperature near the vent rose to 60°C. He also discovered the complex patterns of zigzag trails that the tortoises had created, allowing them to ascend the steep caldera walls to the rim, where moisture-laden mists gave a welcome break from the scorching sun.

Further searches over this extensive volcano eventually revealed that thousands of tortoises survived there. This population has turned out to be the largest and the least disturbed in the whole of the Archipelago. Although Miguel Castro found the remains of twenty-one slaughtered tortoises, demonstrating that the region had indeed been visited by hunters, and who probably introduced the donkeys as beasts of burden, it is the last image we have of the pre-human days. As remarked Ambrose Cowley in 1684, " it is incredible to report how numerous they are."

So there was good and bad news. Yet at least eleven races survived even though some were on the edge of extinction.

What to do?

Nests were still being built on Pinzon, but not a hatchling survived the rats and the hawks.

On the 31st August 1963 a single tortoise was found on Española, eating a cactus pad and surrounded by fifteen goats doing the same thing. Were there more?

Those few tortoises found on San Cristobal. How to increase their numbers?

Always the specter of extinction, sometimes near, sometimes far.

Spurred on by the very real dangers that faced the giant tortoises, the early directors of the Charles Darwin Research Station undertook a three-fold campaign. First the introduced animals, principally goats and pigs, had to be brought under control. This would stem the destruction of nests and allow the vegetation to recover. Second, the reproduction rate of the endangered populations had to be augmented. Third, because the tortoises are regarded as separate races and are a remarkable demonstration of dispersion and adaptation, it was important not to mix them. As it was, a number were kept as pets by local inhabitants and it was important to register these unknown tortoises and if possible bring them under the aegis of the Research Station.

The first task was a matter of hunting campaigns. On Santa Cruz a bounty was paid to hunters to reduce the pig numbers. Organized parties were sent out to islands such as Española to remove the goats.

The third was a matter of organization, record keeping, and obtaining the cooperation of the local community.

The second was more complicated. The limited evidence from San Diego and, later, from Honolulu, indicated that it was possible to breed Galapagos tortoises in captivity. Yet fertility in San Diego seemed to be a problem. Should these places be used as bases of reproduction? Honolulu was 4000 miles away and San Diego not much closer. Logistic problems were enormous and economically it was impossible. Maybe new parasites and diseases might be introduced?

Why not breed them in Galapagos? Here, in the natural environment, they would have the greatest chance of all to breed successfully. With the presence of the Research Station, there was the potential of technical aid and a permanent base. Perhaps the nests could be protected in the wild to prevent their destruction. Later in the incubation period the eggs could be brought to the Station for hatching. Here the tiny youngsters could be cared for and protected from introduced predators until they were strong enough to fend for themselves, even in the face of dogs and pigs. In some of the populations that had been virtually wiped out, the individuals were now so scattered that they could not even find one another to breed. For these it would be necessary to bring a sample number to the Station in the hope that they would breed in captivity.

Thus, with a vision of the recovery of the unique reptiles, the first tentative steps were taken in 1965, when eggs from Pinzon were brought in from the wild. This was the moment of impetus that has led to the present Tortoise Breeding Center on Santa Cruz and its sister center near the village of Villamil on Isabela. A tortoise nest is no easy thing to find. It is merely a slight rise in the ground. But no random spot is this. There are few observations of the complete process of nesting, since it occurs in the late evening and can continue all night. Verbal accounts agree in general on this vital and fascinating procedure. A female seeks out the place with care, sniffing at the ground as she slowly passes over it. She may make a number of trials over a period of several days before the conditions of time and place are correct. The nest excavation, egg-laying, and the filling of the hole are all carried out blind, for the female utilizes exclusively the rear legs for all nest work. To begin with she tears at the soily ground with her powerful nails, rotating the body around the chosen site. Then the hind feet alternate, removing the soil by dragging it up the side of the hole on the top of the foot. As this is taking place copious urine is deposited, perhaps helping to make the soil more workable. The size of the hole varies, but is approximately 37 cm deep and 30 cm wide. At this point she stops work and rests awhile. Then, positioning the small tail and rear part of the shell over the hole, she contracts the egg cavity within her body. Slowly the hard-shelled eggs emerge and fall into the hole. Rarely are they broken, however, for they are lowered down on thick mucus strands, which brake their descent. The hind legs may then be used to check on the eggs. Some say that the foot passes so gently over the eggs that they do not even move, perhaps just checking that they are, in fact, there! At other times it appears that the foot actually adjusts the level of the eggs, or, by gently nudging the eggs here and there, she makes room for the whole clutch. But, by all accounts, the slowly lowered foot, used to clambering over the roughest terrain, is extremely sensitive to the contact with the eggs. For such an enormous and bulky creature there is no doubt that the finesse of touch is truly astounding. Egg numbers vary between 7 and 20, but average nearer the lower end rather than the upper. They are slightly ovoid, measuring about 6 by 5.7 cm. Now the nest is refilled. She carefully brings the moistened soil to the edge of the nest with the rear legs and allows it to dribble down the sides. Finally it is filled. Utilizing the upper side of the foot and ankle, she pats down the surface to form a cap. Within the cap is included fecal material, which the female deposits for this purpose. The scats are moist yet contain much fibrous material, which may help to bind the soil and create the unique characteristics of the nest environment. Some say the plastron is also used to compact the soil. Finally she may bring in a little dry soil from around the nest site. Finished! As the moist soil dries, it forms a hard pan on top of the nest and may help to protect it and help control the moisture content of the nest chamber. A lucky visitor might see a nest being built in the corral housing the Española adult tortoises.

Experience and a good eye are the essential factors for finding nests, but a

Female tortoise laying eggs.

little knowledge of the giant tortoise helps. Under standing the ecology really started with the expedition of the California Academy of Sciences in 1906. It was vastly increased by the early workers at the Charles Darwin Research Station, including the Directors Roger Perry, Peter Kramer, and especially Craig MacFarland, the last of whom had previously studied the tortoises and made them his specialty. These studies, which included those on population sizes, distributions, and nesting habits were essential for the incipient Breeding Center. They were also extremely important in boosting morale, for they showed that the tortoises were capable of high fertility and that the young survived and grew rapidly in captivity, thus dispelling the gloom that the species might now not be able to reproduce in substantial numbers. The studies also showed that the giant tortoises suffered their greatest mortality during the first year of life through natural predation and starvation.

Generally speaking, the giant tortoise breeds during the hot season between January and March. Nest-building commences in June and lasts till December. Hatching time depends on the temperature of the nest chamber, but takes between one hundred and two hundred days.

With this general information and refined by the experience of many field trips, which largely depended on the keen eyes of the early park wardens, information on nesting areas and times for specific islands was slowly gathered. This was vital, for during the first stages of development the embryo was discovered to be extremely delicate and rotating the egg can easily result in the death of the growing tortoise. With time and experience, it was learned that the eggs should not be disturbed for the first ten weeks of incubation. It was important, therefore, to try to locate the nests as soon as possible after the female had laid the eggs so that the nest would not be opened too early. Even if she was not there, the eagle eye of the warden was often able to find the small, disturbed, often slightly raised patches of soil. If a nest was suspected, the surface was gently moved and sometimes the ground was found to be still moist from the urine deposited there during the recent construction of the nest. Even if it was dry, the hard pan that covers the nest from the dried-out soil was sometimes discernible. These later nests gave no clue as to their date of building. Sometimes it was, and still is to this day, necessary to make a calculated guess as to their age.

Park wardens building a stone wall around a nest site.

Because of the delay in removing the eggs, and the constant danger on several islands that pigs and/or dogs would find the nests and destroy them, walls, about one meter high, constructed of local lava rock were build around them. This practice would be later replaced with wire-link netting laid over the nest and anchored by stakes. This seemed to have less effect on the natural incubation of the eggs. Also it had been found that pigs were capable of demolishing the walls yet were defeated by the link fencing.

When the eggs were removed from the nests, between ten and fifteen weeks after they were laid, they had to be treated with kid gloves for transport to the Research Station. Each egg was marked with a cross to indicate its upper side and, embedded in sawdust, was carried in that position. Of course, to complicate matters, most nests were not to be found conveniently close to the coast, but way inland, which involved hours of hiking through closed scrub and dense spiny vegetation, in which Galapagos abounds! From the shore it was often many hours in a small boat on a lumpy sea before the precious eggs were set in quiet surroundings at the Research Station.

But where were they to be kept, now that they were out of the protection of the nest in which they were originally placed?

As a first tentative measure, an underground nest chamber was constructed. This had a rat-proof cover placed over it. Every two weeks the cover was removed and the eggs examined. As hatching approached, the eggs turned darker and flaking of the shell occurred. Hatching eggs were placed in the Director's office in a glass bowl, which kept ants at bay. The hatching process

In order to reach nesting areas, the park wardens must often cut their way through spiny vegetation in a hot land with no water.

takes an average of three days. The shell is broken with an "egg tooth" on the tortoise's nose and the exit from the case is aided with movements of the legs and feet. Once born and dry, the tiny tortoises were placed in a rearing pen constructed of chicken-wire mesh.

When the tortoise leaves the egg, it still has the remains of the yolk sac attached to its stomach, from which the hatchling still derives a rich proteinaceous food. With increasing experience, it was found that survival was enhanced if the hatchling was left in the dark until the sac was absorbed and the tortoise's shell had straightened and hardened. This seemed to mimic what happens with nests made in the wild, where the newborn hatchlings resided some time in the nest chamber to toughen up before digging their way out. To differentiate the young, both individually and by population, they were all numbered with paint. To measure growth, they were weighed periodically.

About the same time that the first eggs were being brought from Pinzon in 1965, the

Peter Kramer, an early director of the Research Station,
eagerly looks for signs of hatching eggs.

Station was receiving tortoises from several sources. Two were from Española, since the population was thought to be so small that any found were brought into captivity. Six came from San Cristobal, another population believed to be in a critical condition. Another source were the unknown tortoise "pets" from the villages. It became an obligation to register these animals and an agreement was signed affirming that, if the "owner" did not require the animals anymore, they would be cared for by the Station. Now they were arriving! The first pens, built of lava stones, were constructed just behind the beach. It is still worth the walk under the arch of button mangrove and manzanillo trees to see the evidence of the early efforts to save the giant tortoises.

One reason for building the pens near the village was a strong belief that it should be possible for the public to see the tortoises and have explained the sad state in which humans had left many of the remaining populations of these magnificent creatures. To this end, it was, at that time, the obligation of scientists to leave their microscopes and chemicals, reports and proposals, to tell the tale to enquiring visitors! It was also important that the work of the Station should gain support from the local community. It should be remembered that tortoises were still being killed and eaten locally, and others stolen by visitors. Also the new laws of the National Park were starting to be applied, which to some extent limited the activities of the settlers, who were used to a "free and easy" lifestyle. Conservation needed no enemies.

The tortoise pens at the Research Station give visitors an excellent opportunity to be in the company of these prehistoric reptiles.

Slowly the number of adult Española tortoises grew. In 1966 there were five, two males and three females, an increase of three on the original two. Females were being found with lichen growing on their backs, indicating that they had not mated for many years, perhaps decades!

Young Pinzon tortoises were now growing up and each year more eggs were brought in for hatching. To give them a head start, it was considered that they should remain at the Station for five years, after which time it was hoped that they were immune from attacks by the introduced rats and even their natural predators, the hawks. Also at that age they would have exceeded the critical first year, when maximum mortality occurred.

The year 1970 was a golden year for tortoises. On the tenth of December, the first twenty Pinzon youngsters made the return trip to their island home. They had never seen it, only felt its heated soil as they lay in the ground as developing eggs five years previously. How would they react? Would they survive? Was the dream of saving dying populations to be a reality? They were liberated in the highlands of the island and seemed fine, strutting out into the wild country. Field workers stayed with them for ten days, during which time they seemed to be quite at home, eating and successfully constructing their shallow night scrapes in the stony soil. Then they were left alone to nature, their instincts, and chance. Several months later, in February of 1971, a visit was made by anxious field workers and a number of the repatriates were found. They had put on weight and were doing just fine. Not long after, all of them were found and they were twice as heavy.

In the Española pen things also took a good turn. Three nests were constructed in 1970 with a content of thirty-two eggs. If fertility was up, this might triple, even quadruple, the total number of extant tortoises from that island.

75% fertility and 20 tortoise hatchlings!

The system was beginning to work. The declining trends of the tortoise populations could be reversed.

By now the Station was handling many eggs from five different islands: Española, Pinzon, San Cristobal, Santa Cruz, and Santiago. The old subterranean nest chamber had gone. In its place, a row of six solar incubators, with a total capacity of eighty eggs or so, was constructed behind the beach head close to the original tortoise pens. (These can still be viewed as you walk past the Director's house just behind the beach, where, in the breeding season, they are used by female marine iguanas, who perhaps inspect them as potential nest sites of their own.) Today the incubators are falling to pieces, but some of the black ink lingers on the labels. "*chatamensis*" (San Cristobal) and "Pinzon" can still be made out. The construction of the incubators was intended to simulate the nest chambers and were heated by the sun. The design is still quite easy to determine.

The original solar incubators, which attempted to simulate natural nest conditions, are now falling into decay. However, in their day, they showed that these semi - artificial conditions could produce a high hatching rate.

Doors allowed access to the "nest chamber," above which was a sheet of perforated corrugated asbestos, on top of which was soil, and the whole arrangement capped by a metal sheet painted black. One of the doors had a glass sheet behind it, which allowed the "nest" to be examined without affecting the humidity or temperature. What is not visible today is the bowl of water that was maintained in the "nest chamber" to keep the air moist, for, although the egg shells are hard, they still absorb water and need to do so for the well-being of the embryo. The temperature in the boxes varied with the sunshine and could not be maintained easily at any particular level. Still, it was felt that it should not rise above 35°C and that the average temperature was considered about 29°C. If the "nests" were becoming too hot, the door could be opened. As in all solutions to problems in out - of - the - way places, it had to be simple, constructed of local materials, and, if possible, inexpensive!

Today female marine iguanas enjoy a rest in the abandoned beach incubators - perhaps even looking at them as potential nesting sites.

However the young were still being raised in the chicken-wire pens by the trees on the beach. This appears to have been a mistake, for, although the fertility was high, too many of the hatchlings were dying of what seemed to be digestion problems with food becoming impacted in their intestines. Was it the cool breezes off the sea and the cool dampness of the *garúa* (fine rain) that was chilling the hatchlings? Perhaps they needed to be warmer. Because of these difficulties, which were limiting the success of the efforts to save the tortoises, it was decided to look for funds to construct a Tortoise House. With the support of the San Diego Zoological Society, this was achieved, and, in 1969, work began. Within a year it was finished. A building as unique as the tortoises themselves, with thirteen sides, designed and built by the manager of the Station, Rolf Sievers.

All tortoises from 1970 onward were raised within its confines. Internally it was divided into pens which radiated out from the center. But the center itself was an open area, which allowed visitors to view the baby tortoises through the glass fronts of the pens. Also there was a panel with photographs and explanations describing the project. In the very center was a box for donations! For the visitors it gave an excellent show.

The pens themselves had concrete floors and in one corner 1000-watt bulbs gave heat and light ten hours a day. (Power had always been a problem and the Research Station relied very strongly on its own capacity to provide it through diesel generators.) Survival in general improved, but it was still felt that there was something lacking that could improve things further. Perhaps sunlight and warmth were still dogging success, for although the tortoises were being raised in the Galapagos Islands, the village at Academy Bay (now Puerto Ayora) can be covered with cloud for months on end,

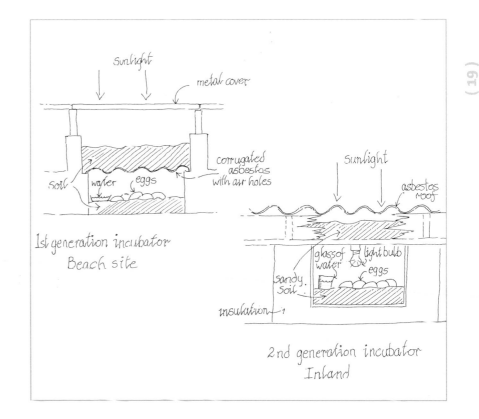

especially in the cool season, and perhaps is not typical of the areas where tortoises hatch in the wild. Maybe the tortoises needed the sun on their backs when it was available. To try to improve this, rat-proof balconies were added to the house (now called the *casona*) in 1972. These were connected via tunnels to the pens inside. This allowed the tortoises to amble out into the sunshine. In the same year additional pens were constructed at the rear of the building, to house the ever-increasing number of hatchlings.

During these formative years the other prongs of the tortoise conservation program were going ahead — the retrieval of unidentified tortoises and the control of introduced animals.

The calling in of all unidentified tortoises was successful and was greatly aided by the cooperation of the Port Captains, who understood the problem and were, moreover, the most powerful people in the islands at the time. Eventually over sixty were housed at the Station.

The growing number of tortoises required more corrals and these were built in their present positions inland from the Tortoise House. They are about 50 by 20 meters. The walls are constructed of black lava rocks, built on the rough natural terrain with its own native vegetation. In each pen is a pool of water, for tortoises love to bathe, and a feeding platform. Today, the two most inland house the fifteen Española adults, two contain the unknowns, and the fifth is home to Lonesome George and two potential, but neglected, wives from the north of Isabela.

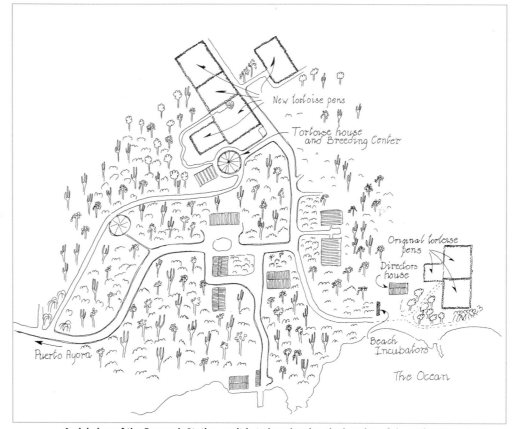

Aerial view of the Research Station, as it is today, showing the location of the various tortoise pens.

By the early 1970s the Galapagos National Park Service, within Ecuador's Ministry of Agriculture, and administered in the islands by its first two representatives, José Villa and Juan Black, was gaining strength and was proving to be an enormous force in helping to solve the other issue - introduced animals.

There was no question as to the damage that was being caused by these mammalian invaders and there was really only one solution. They had to be removed.

Extremely rare Española adults, 15 in number, live in two adjacent
pens, where they breed. The three males and twelve females are the source of
nearly 1000 tortoises repatriated to their home islands, Española.

If they stayed, irreparable changes would be made to the islands' ecosystems. As it was, some of the islands were becoming deserts. The park wardens, about as cheerful and tough a breed as could be found anywhere in the world, set about this heroic task with a determination that was soon to guarantee success in the removal of goats on Santa Fe in 1971, on Rabida in 1972, Española in 1978, and Marchena in 1979. It was on one of these hunting trips, in 1972, that the lone survivor of the Pinta tortoise, Lonesome George, was brought back to the Station. This old male had been seen the year before by Joseph Vagvolgyi and his wife, whilst they were out studying endemic snails, some of them almost as rare as George himself. The goats on Pinta had increased enormously since their introduction in 1959, with 26,000 goats being removed in 1972, the first year of hunting on Pinta.

Alone and surrounded by devastated vegetation. Lonesome George spends
his last days on Pinta before being removed to the Research Station in 1972.

Without the control of introduced animals, the Tortoise Breeding Program was useless. To spend years raising hundreds of young tortoises only to put them into an inhospitable or dangerous environment was pointless. The success of both programs was vital in the effort to restore the ecosystem in which the giant tortoises played a major part.

By 1976 the incubation chambers on the beach were suffering from the effects of the salt air and, in preference to repairing them, it was decided to build new ones near the outside rearing pens behind the Tortoise House. In many ways the construction differed little from those on the beach, but the total capacity was more than doubled. Now there were twelve "nests" built in four units. Each "nest" was capable of holding about twenty eggs. One modification was the installation of a small light bulb to help stabilize the temperature in the chamber.

Tortoises were now coming out of the Breeding Center at a pace, which, at a previous date, was only a dream. In 1975 forty-two were repatriated, in 1976 eighty-one, in 1984 seventy-four. The system of locating the nests, protecting them, excavating, and transporting the eggs to the Station was now almost a routine affair. The eggs were being incubated, hatchlings moved to the Tortoise House, and finally, after a hardening off period, when the tortoises spent all their time outside on the natural rough ground, they were returned to their true homes, the remote islands of the Archipelago.

Second generation solar incubators were built further inland and electric bulbs were used to augment heat at night.

A general view of the breeding center in 1999. In the background is the old tortoise rearing house.

Sadly the number of Española adults had stopped rising. The total population was represented by two males and twelve females. As close as you want to get to extinction! But they were breeding well and the females were building nests in the special soily areas that had been provided for them in the pens. Moreover, in April of 1975, for the first time, seventeen five-year-olds were repatriated. At that moment, the total population was doubled. It was lucky that the sex ratio of the adults was skewed towards females, for that meant that most animals were producing eggs. The down side was the severe lack of genetic variability, a dangerous potential. This situation was modified slightly by the arrival of a crate, on August 8, 1978, at the Research Station. Within it, and blinking in the strong sunlight, was a male Española tortoise! He had been located at the San Diego Zoo, and, from his distinctive form and size, had been given the blessing as to his origin, largely based on the work of Tom Fritts, who had made a study of the morphology of Galapagos shell shapes. On the basis of this information, the curator of herpetology at San Diego, James Bacon, recognizing the inestimable value of the genetic component of this tortoise in the saving of the Española race, agreed to his return. After *fifty years* of absence, he had come home. He too bred well - and still does. Interestingly, recent genetic tests have confirmed his identity.

There can be no doubt that the biology of the giant tortoise has saved them. Their extreme longevity and long breeding life, coupled with their ability to survive in extraordinarily harsh conditions, has defied the attempts to destroy them.

But it was not all without problems. The hatching rate, averaging about 25%, was still disappointingly low. The hatchlings in the Tortoise House were also suffering losses as well. Were the eggs too hot? Too cold? Too wet? Too dry? The hatchlings, even though provided with the outside balconies, were perhaps not really enjoying a natural life. Were the concrete floors, though easy to clean, part of that unnaturalness? Perhaps a little dirt where the hatchlings could "roost" at night might be important. Diet might also be a problem.

Although diseases are uncommon, there were problems with prolapses, which were cured with a truly local herbal remedy of boiled hibiscus or plantain leaves. There were also problems with the skin that appeared to be related to fungus and treated with fungicides. In the cold season, the young animals sometimes suffered from shaking and a softening of the shell accompanied by its deformation.

Then a completely new issue arose. What sex were all these children of the giants? At birth you could not tell them apart visually.

This might sound a curious question, since we, as mammals, are used to the fixed status of our gender from the moment of conception. A male is a male. A female is a female. But is that true of all life? In chromosomal terms, a human male is termed heterogametic, with the potential to produce gametes (sex cells) containing either of two sex chromosomes, termed X and Y. A female is homogametic in producing gametes which all contain X type sex chromosomes. These are unchangeable after conception. Thus the system is clear cut. But in the late 1960s, studies on the   rainbow lizard of Central Africa showed that the sex ratio (the number of male to female hatchlings expressed as a ratio) in a nest of these Old World reptiles appeared to be dependent on temperature. Studies through the 1970s began to show that this characteristic was very common amongst reptilian groups including turtles, crocodiles, and even the

Cool for males, warmer for females. This is the norm for temperature - determined sex in many reptiles!

(23)

ancient-lineaged tuataras of New Zealand. Some species show the typical form, that is, males produced at low temperatures and females at higher ones — the mnemonic, left with me by a visiting veterinarian, "cool dudes and hot babes," may help the reader remember which way round it is. The European pond turtle, for example, produces all males below 27.5°C, mostly males at 27.5-28°C, both sexes at 28-29°C, mostly females at 29-29.5°C, and finally, all are females above 29.5°C. Below and above these limits, developmental problems begin to occur, which eventually result in total failure. Somewhere between these temperatures is the so-called pivotal temperature, at which fifty percent are males and fifty percent are females. But nothing is simple. Crocodilians show exactly the opposite trend and snapping turtles, amongst others, have two pivotal points, with females produced at high and low points and males produced in between.

How does it work? No one is absolutely sure, but the principal theory at the moment suggests that various levels of heat act differentially on genes that produce enzymes (catalysts), which convert steroids (close relatives to cholesterol) from one form (male) to another (female). This is understandable when one considers that androgens (male hormones) and estrogens (female hormones) are extremely closely related in chemical form.

The hypothesis is that testosterone, the steroid, is deposited in the egg by the mother. Dependent on the temperature of incubation at the temperature-sensitive stage of development, which has been found to be one-third to one-half of the incubation period, enzymes may change testosterone to estradiol, an estrogen, or 5-alpha reductase, an androgen. Either of these enzymes may attach to the embryonic gonads at appropriate reception points, triggering the development of ovaries or testes. These in turn will produce their own hormones, which will further emphasize the animal's future gender.

For this system to have survived for millions of years, there ought to be some benefit to males and females hatched at different incubation temperatures. This seems to be born out by experiments conducted on snapping turtles. Males and females born at some point above and below the pivotal temperature survive better that those born at it. Moreover, the pivotal temperature and those at which more abundant males and females are born are, like so much in nature, subject to the forces of natural selection, since the genes involved are open to changes through time, thus allowing the species to adapt to long-term climatic change.

As more and more studies revealed the commonplace of this remarkable sex-determining mechanism, it began to niggle at the minds of scientists and conservationists working with the giant tortoises that perhaps the dozens of tortoises already released and those being prepared for release were all Susans and no Peters, or vice-versa. It had been expected that about half would be females, since this is normal in many reproductive systems. If it could be shown that temperature sex determination did occur, there might be an advantage in the future, whatever had happened in the past, since it might be possible to artificially produce more females than males and therefore boost the egg production and reduce the time to create large wild populations from repatriated tortoises. The ideal ratio was considered to be two-thirds females to one-third males.

The big question was: Does temperature sex determination occur in the giant tortoises of Galapagos and, if it does, at what temperature should the eggs be incubated to produce the desired result?

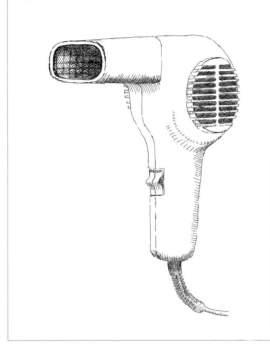

An ingenious heat source for the latest thermostatically controlled incubators.

It was obvious that this question and the health problems that were occurring in the Tortoise House should be resolved as soon as possible.

The experiments began in 1986 under the supervision of herpetologist Howard Snell, with the body of the work being carried out by Cruz Márquez and Solanda Rea, both still involved in the breeding program thirteen years later, in 1999. A further key figure in this panorama was Bill Gutzke from the University of Tennessee, who had been working on temperature sex determination. His specific work would be the sexing of the hatchlings. The objectives were twofold; first, to resolve the above question and second, to improve the whole breeding system so that more tortoises from a given number of eggs could be returned to the wild.

In order to solve the problem, it was necessary to incubate the eggs at specific temperatures and then determine the sex of the hatchlings.

But the obvious question arose — how to ensure that the temperature remained constant. This was impossible in the case of the solar-heated incubators, in which the temperature varied with cloud cover and the season of the year. In order to guarantee the reliability of the study, a new approach had to be made. This was facilitated to some extent by the availability of a somewhat more dependable power supply that was now being offered in the village. In the early 1970s, it was four hours a day but the length of time had been increasing by leaps and bounds and was now at eighteen hours. In addition to this, the Station still maintained its own power plant. Now it was possible to consider using electrical appliances on a broader field. A thermostatically controlled incubator? That would be exactly the answer. In fact the only answer. Thus an expensive and rather cumbersome apparatus was brought from the United States and finally landed at Puerto Ayora to be installed at the Station. Although used in the early experiments, the equipment was not tolerant of the sometimes violent voltage surges, the black-outs, and the harsh environmental conditions of coastal Galapagos. In addition, its spare parts were expensive and had to be imported. Necessity being the mother of invention, Howard Snell searched his mind for an inexpensive and

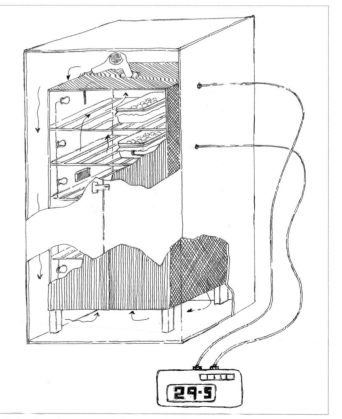

Today, in order to control the sex ratio of the hatchlings, the temperature of the incubators is controlled to within 1 degree centigrade.

reliable alternative. He needed a simple source of heat that could be controlled. He hit upon a unique answer — a hair dryer! This could inject warmth into the air within a closed area and be thermostatically controlled. This led to a design that has stood the test of time and is in present use. The outside appearance is of a large wooden clothes cupboard. Inside is a second chamber or cupboard around which, and within which, the air is circulated by a small fan. A thermostat controls the hair dryer, which has a remarkably long life, considering its originally intended use, yet is cheap to replace and available locally. Trays of eggs are installed on the various shelves of the inner case. An electronic temperature gauge registers the heat every three hours.

To begin with, three batches of eggs were incubated at three different temperatures, quite far apart, but based on evidence gathered from turtles elsewhere: 25.5°C, 29.5°C, and 33.5°C. This test would probably answer the question as to whether sex was determined by heat. The answer was unequivocal. Yes! At 25.5°C, 84% were males. At 29.5°C, 33% were males and 67% females. At 33.5°C, none of the eggs developed properly, or at all.

A further experiment carried out the following year, 1987, confined the temperatures further, 27°C, 29°C, and 31°C. These not only confirmed the experiments of the previous year, but also gave a much more precise idea of the pivotal temperature, which lies near 29°C. On the basis of this, it was decided that the ideal temperatures for the desired sex ratio would be 28°C and 29.5°C, since those incubated very near the pivotal temperature might be at a disadvantage.

But how was the sex to be confirmed? Adults can be distinguished by the shape of the plastron (the underside of the shell). Males are concave and females convex. But morphologically the baby tortoises all look very similar. Some believed that it was possible to differentiate them by counting the small scales on the tail, a number which is larger in adult males than in females. But this was very dependent on the observer and there seemed to be such an overlap that the system could not be counted upon. The secret had to be in examining the gonads, or reproductive organs, where structure and texture would give away the answer. But these are inside the animal. How to get at them? Killing the animals was not an option, since each hatchling was so valuable and anyway a technique was required that could be used on future batches of baby tortoises. The answer lay in a process known as laparotomy (*lapara* is Greek for flank or loin). This involves a very small incision at the inside base of the rear leg and the insertion of a tiny stainless steel tube, through which the internal organs can be seen, for the tube has its own beam of light. By this process, Bill Gutzke was able to view the nature of the gonads, even the developing oviducts of the females. Through this procedure, which has no lasting effect on the hatchlings, it was possible for the whole breeding program to continue with a degree of confidence unheard of before. Today, further experiments by Elliott Jacobson, from the University of Florida, are underway to find out if it is possible to differentiate the sex of tortoise hatchlings by hormone levels in the blood which would avoid even making a small incision in their bodies. This involves correlating the observed sex of the hatchlings (through the laparotomy operation) with an analysis of the blood. Analysis of the data continues, but the results are not as yet conclusive.

The temperature experiments also had another payoff. The hatchling rate was greatly increased over the old incubation system, which was about 25%. From this time on it rose to an annual average of 50%. A 100% increase in tortoises born, doubling the efforts of the program!

At the same time that these experiments were taking place, comparative studies were made on systems for raising the hatchlings. Some were raised in the Tortoise House, with its concrete floors and outside balconies, whilst others were kept in the outside pens, which were amongst natural vegetation and were sunnier, fresher places. In a short space of time, the figures clearly showed that the outside life was preferred. These animals were — and are — kept in the soily, open-topped enclosures for about one and a half years for their own protection. At night rat-proof mesh covers are placed over them. From then on they spend all the time roaming the area around the pens, but still enclosed within a wider area. The stony, earthy, sunny, shady environment allows them to stretch their legs and tone their muscles, choose the sun or the shade, seek out night roosts, climb hills and descend valleys. In fact they do the things tortoises have to do to survive. Health problems also declined.

The question of diet was also examined. Luckily, Linda Cayot had studied the food of Galapagos tortoises — in the particularly trying times of the 1983 Niño season, when tortoise country was a running river — and could come up with some answers. Papaya, which had been fed to the youngsters, was found to be potentially lethal. What has become the standard fare is a mixture of vegetative matter from herbs and shrubs, some of them native, some introduced. There is the saltbush from the coast, the diminutive purple-flowered wanderer, *Commicarpus*, several composites, a member of the coffee family, nettles, plantains, a red-flowered legume, and otoy, a cultivated starchy plant in the arum lily family, otherwise known as elephant ears. Nor should be forgotten the pads of the oputia tree cactus. Spiny, but a treat to a tortoise! Because the Station is situated in the dry coastal region of the island, contracts are made with local people to bring plants from the wetter highlands. It was also discovered that tortoises can become obese. This condition may be injurious both to their health and to their reproductive potential. The adults therefore are only fed three times a week.

The old tortoise house did have one element that was irreplaceable. It protected the baby tortoises from theft — there always seems to be a demand for giant tortoises in the outside world — and it protected them from rats. Still, the new enhanced survival rate more than compensates for these potential risks.

Although the basic details of the incubators are described above, a few more details are needed to appreciate them fully. The eggs, each marked with a cross to indicate its upper side, an "N" number for the nest, an "H" number for the egg, and a "T" number for the number of eggs in a nest, are placed in vermiculite, an inert, layered silicate, which expands greatly when heated to form a light, cellular material with the feel of Styrofoam. This material has several advantages. In the first place, it can be cleaned and reused. Equally important is the fact that it can absorb water and give it off in a predictable way. Since the incubation period is in excess of four months, the vermiculite is changed every thirty days. At each renewal, 350 cc of water are absorbed by 1000 grams of vermiculite. This is sufficient for about twenty eggs. Each batch is placed in a plastic bowl, covered with a sheet of transparent plastic. This allows the eggs to be observed frequently without changing their microclimate. However, should a damaged egg be seen, and this is often accompanied by the growth of fungus, it must be removed immediately before the whole batch is damaged. The system of fans, 1500-watt hair dryer, and thermostat are capable of maintaining the temperature within 1°C of that desired. The readout of temperature gives a warning should anything fail. There are light bulbs installed as an emergency measure should there be a delay in replacing a damaged hair dryer. At the present time, there are two incubators, one running at 28°C and the other at 29.5°C, with the eggs from each tortoise population divided between them. The incubation times are near 125 days for the higher temperature and about 150 for the lower.

Once hatched, the tortoises are left in the plastic bowls for several days, still at the incubation temperature. From there they are removed and placed in the *caja oscura* (dark box), which is at ambient temperature. Here they harden off for thirty days with no food or water. This really is no hardship for them, since they are still living off the yolk sac, which is rapidly being absorbed. The box is square, with half a meter on all sides. The floor is covered with vermiculite and three air holes allow the passage of fresh air.

At the end of this time the tortoises are off to the rearing pens. These can be seen from the tourist trail. Often there are many different age groups. The very young and small are in the pens, where they receive food and water. Older ones are outside roaming the whole enclosure.

Today is the fifth of January 1999. To date over 2000 young tortoises have been repatriated to different islands.

Inside the Rearing Center, which today is run by personnel from the National Park Service, there is a constant bustle. It's not so much that there are a lot of active people, but the whole floor of the center, including the cement bases of the pens, the rocky ground that surrounds them, and the areas under the bushes, seem to be on the move. And be careful with your feet! The fact is tortoises are everywhere, striding between the pens, climbing the steep rocky slopes, chewing on a fallen cactus pad, drinking and bathing alongside the small Darwin's finches, whose whirring wings send a spray of droplets onto the reptiles' horny shells. There are hundreds of tortoises and they come in all sizes. The smallest, a few centimeters long, are inside the pens, where they are dozing in the sun, or clambering on a pile of small stones in the center, where their water supply is found. Outside are the big ones, some in excess of twenty-five centimeters and on the verge of being repatriated to their island of origin. One of them is wandering — and they can be remarkably quick on their feet — along the concrete base which surrounds the pens. There is a drop of half a meter or so to the hard ground below. Oughtn' t they put a guardrail around to stop them falling off? He comes to the edge and obviously wishes to get down, but, sensing the drop, he hesitates with outstretched neck weaving back and forth. Realizing a danger, he retreats. After moving along the base, this procedure is repeated. Still too high. At the fourth attempt, and the drop is now about twenty-five centimeters, he studies the situation, edges forward so that the front of the shell is over the fall yet the hind feet are still in charge

After hatching, the baby tortoises are placed in a "dark box", (here with the cover removed) for a hardening off period of thirty days.

As they ages, the tortoises are placed in the natural area that surrounds the pens.
A recently fallen cactus provides a fine natural meal - and water!

For the first year or so , demost risky time for a young tortoise,
special protection an care are given to the hatchlings.

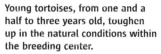

Young tortoises, from one and a
half to three years old, toughen
up in the natural conditions within
the breeding center.

...Fausto Llerena working with recently hatched tortoises.

of the situation, and decides to go. Tucking the head in with the forefeet braced, he tilts the body up with the back feet and moves it forward. Soon the center of gravity is over the edge. Retracting the hind legs, the shell tips forward. Bump, half way down, a projecting stone partially breaks the fall. Bump. All the way down and right side up. In a moment, the head is out and he's off for a drink. This is no brute animal, but a calculating being. What happens if they turn upside down? Given the slightest projection or roughness they manage to catch it with a foot and twist themselves over again!

Threading my way through the reptile throng, I arrive at a small building which houses the incubators. Inside, Fausto Llerena, who is and has been the life and soul of the care lavished on every tortoise for many years, is making notes on a list of one hundred and fifty tortoises that will be released in a few days on Española, a trip I will accompany them on. At his right stand the two incubators. There is a constant whir of the little circulating fans in each one. This is punctuated every so often by a slightly higher pitched noise as one of the hair dryers turns on in response to the thermostat switch. "Several have hatched over the weekend," he says, glancing at the left hand incubator, which has "28°C" written on it. The second chamber lies inside the outer doors and has a capacity of one hundred and fifty eggs. Several colored bowls are visible. Peering in, I see seven small tortoises in the red one. They're from Española and are actively scrabbling about. They were born on the 30th of December 1998 so now they are five days old and about to be placed in the dark box. These creatures are fascinating. But what catches the eye is an egg that has just hatched, or

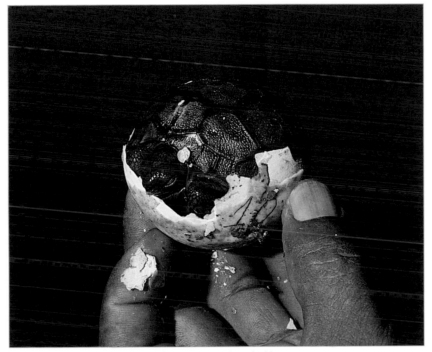

On the verge of hatching.. A tortoise fits like a sphere inside egg.

Finally, after an incubation period of over one hundred and twenty days, a tortoise breaks free from the eggshell, wich is partially embedded in vermiculite.

The active youngsters are removed from the incubator.

rather is in the process of hatching. The upper surface has broken away and the tortoise sits, black and curled into an almost perfect sphere as if the eggshell still contained it. Fausto wishes to look at it and places it in my hand for a moment's safe keeping. I heft the creature and am surprised at its weight. It gives me the impression of a largish billiard ball. The shell scutes, the horny outer covering of the skeleton, are rough in texture and definitively bordered by a broad black edging. On the underside the pale yellow, semi-transparent yolk sac is attached to the midline of the body. After an inspection, it is carefully placed back on the remaining piece of egg shell. Here it will remain, gathering strength, for it is a fragile child at this stage. I am privileged to see some of the miraculous changes that normally take place in the pitch black within the nest chamber on some wild land on the slopes of ancient volcanoes. It is striking to see the change in its boisterous siblings, only a few days older. The shells have flattened out and hardened to a dark brown. It almost seems that I have seen a tortoise created before my very eyes, for these youngsters are similar to the adults except, of course, in size.

At birth, the tiny tortoise is delicate and still relies on the attached egg yolk for growth and sustenance.

Dressed as a tiny knight in burnished armor, a five-day-old tortoise looks remarkably like an adult — except in size.

Each is given a colored identification number.....

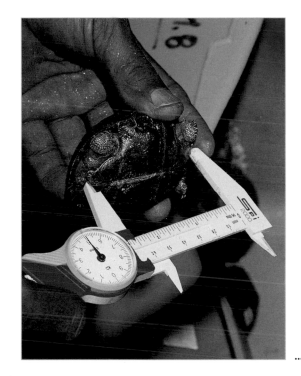

.....is measured for length.....

Now they are numbered, weighed and measured.

•#58	curved length	8.9 cm.
	curved width	9.6 cm.
	length of plastron	7.1 cm.
	weight	93 gms.
•#59	curved length	8.7 cm.
	curved width	9.7 cm.
	length of plastron	7.0 cm.
	weight	86 gms.
•#60	and so on.........	

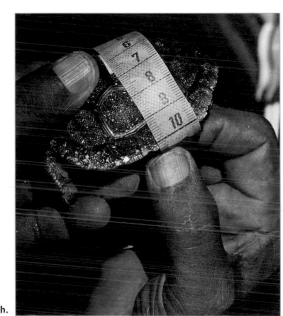

.....and girth.

The underside of the tortoises has changed. Where the yolk sac was is now a closing yellowish slit. Once the data-gathering is complete, which includes painting a blue number on the back end of the shell (blue for Española), the top of the black box is removed and the seven tortoises, representing almost half of the total adult population of the island, are placed inside on the bed of vermiculite. The season must have been good, for there is hardly room for them amongst all the other new hatchlings. Things are looking up for the giant tortoise!

Two days later with sweat pouring off the faces of even the hardened park wardens, we climb a small rocky outcrop to take a short break. To the north lies the sea, blue and calm. To the east of the beach at Gardner Bay, which we left an hour ago, are three small islands, the largest of which is also called Gardner. All around us, and beneath us, like a gray stubbly beard, lies the dry vegetation on the north slope of the island of Española. Trees, shrubs, and herbs are taking a rest before the imminent rainy season. There is no sound except our own. I comment how remarkable it was that Nestor had found this spot, since he had not been here for twenty-three years and the rampant growth of the 1998 Niño season had obliterated the trail. He smiles and says, "to old music the compass runs true." All those years ago he came with the first group of tortoises to be repatriated to this island. That was the year when this land, one of the most ancient of the Galapagos, once again felt the tread of young tortoise feet for the first time in perhaps seventy-five years. Some of them are now half a meter long.

On the way up a tortoise is found. This animal was raised at the Station and released six years ago, demonstrating its capacity to survive in their natural environment after a "soft" upbringing. Already the "saddle" is apparent.

Park warden Néstor Cadena judges the lay of the land.

A quick swig of water and we must move on higher into the interior before the sun gets too hot. Each park warden swings up a backpack loaded with a bulging sack. "Product of Canada," they announce. But inside is pure Galapagos which no money could buy, for each man carries thirteen young tortoises — going home! Between them all we have over one hundred, or six times the total adult population back at the Research Station. I cannot be more overjoyed to realize that the dream of the early conservationists is being fulfilled. After the near mortal blow dealt to the tortoises on this island by the whalers of the last century, who may even have followed the same dry water bed we now walk up, in their determined search for the beautiful little saddlebacks, the trend is now reversed and the land is being recolonized by these gentle reptiles.

Howard Snell made an exploratory trip yesterday to find a new location to release the young tortoises, for, at the old site, several kilometers to the west, there are signs that young opuntia cactus, which are a very rare sight, are now growing there.

This is good news indeed, for the golden-red trunked plants may be very important for the survival of many tortoises. The adult opuntias are also uncommon, for many of them were destroyed by the feral goats, before they were removed, and it is further suspected that the absence of the tortoises prevented successful reproduction of the cactus. It is quite possible that the large, hard seeds germinate more readily if they first pass through the stomach of the reptiles. If this is now beginning to happen, spreading the tortoises out may help the cactus forest to grow as well. The plants themselves are magnificent, with a flaring, domed head of pads, rather like a field mushroom, spread out from the broad, two-meter-high, vertical trunk. Under this canopy, which acts like a water storage tank for the tortoises, giving up its valuable liquid as the pads fall, the shade is delicious. The tortoises think so, too, for outside there is a blazing heat. Now, in early January, large, yellow flowers gild these havens in an otherwise daunting landscape.

Large cactus are important in the arid land of Española, as they provide vital shade, food and water.

We finally brave the crest and curve around the rocky volcanic hill to our left. Now there are open patches, where grass will grow when the rain comes. A cool sea breeze is coming up the other side of the hill, and, as we pass the first large cactus, suddenly there is the ocean, silver and glittering in the distance. We start downhill into a large, shallow valley. Rocky outcrops dot the rim to the south and west. In the middle of the valley, a lake accumulates in the very wet years. There was one here last year, 1998. No doubt the tortoises will manage to cope with its muddy, rocky shoreline as they enjoy a drink and a wallow alongside the ducks and the bathing finches.

Finally the tortoises are released. Cruz Márquez records each release and the number of the pit tag is registered.

Soon we are amongst a grove of opuntias, *tunas* they call them locally. Several have fallen and the pads lie heaped up and many are sprouting. Just down slope there is a patch of muyuyo trees, green leafed with yellow trumpet-shaped flowers dancing in the breeze. This is a nice spot — from a reptilian point of view. Howard stops and looks at Cruz Márquez, a Station herpetologist and a key figure in the ongoing supervision of the Tortoise Breeding Program. "What do you think? Down amongst the muyuyos or perhaps here near the fallen pads?" Cruz slowly passes a gaze over the landscape, using his long experience to judge the area. "These pads will give them a good start." With this simple statement, the decision is made.

Before release each tortoise has its pit tag number read and recorded.

This is the moment. As each tortoise is carefully extracted from the sack, its small dark eyes will see an island home that it has never known before. Its survival will depend on the good start it had at the Station, its instincts, the island ecosystem, and perhaps luck. Looking at this scene, I suddenly felt a slight panic, a chill on this bright sunny day. In the nick of time this island was saved from becoming another Easter Island, which was made lonely and destitute of its natural life by the introduction of animals and the destruction of its ecosystem, where the wind and sun play but the land a waste.

On her back and with feet waving in the air, a tortoise is scrutinized with an instrument looking very much like a clothes iron. It is in fact an electronic reading device similar to those used in supermarkets to read bar-coded prices. It is searching for a tiny tag, named a pit tag, that was inserted by syringe under the skin of the tortoise six months ago. The number will be the lifelong identification for this animal. From this personal number, it will be possible to monitor the progress of each animal, its growth rate, location, and finally a female's reproductive status, should she be found again. Relating this back to its days at the Station will provide vital information for controlling the future success of the program. The pit tag is replacing an ingenious counting method, used both for juveniles and adults, which involved cutting notches into the border of the shell. These represented a unique numbering system. It was a little unsightly and, worse, with time the notches become obscured. Finally, the warden rights the animal and, with remarkable care, places it atop the pile of pads. This may be the last human touch that these animals will feel in a lifetime that may exceed one hundred years. Once placed on the ground, the tortoises sit quietly for a while, for it has been quite a trip.

Two days ago they were taken from the rearing pens to be placed in large wooden boxes, fifty in each one. The boxes were transported by truck to the dock, where they took a short dinghy ride to one of the Park Service patrol boats, the *Belle Vie*. That same night, at eleven pm, the vessel left for Española with the three boxes of tortoises, six park wardens, plus Howard and Cruz from the Station. It took seven hours of

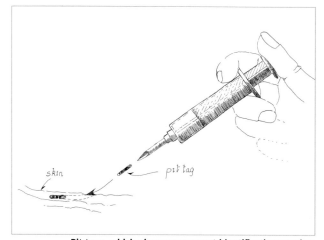

Pit tags, which give a permanent identification number to each tortoise, are inserted under the skin by using a syringe and needle.

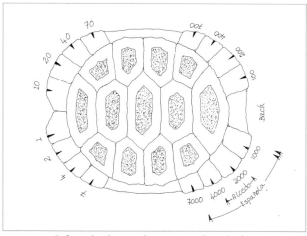

Before pit tags, notches were cut into the four corners of the carapace to give a unique number. This system gives any number from 1 to 10.000.

Carrying a precious cargo of tortoises, a park patrol boat approaches Española.

sailing to complete the fifty-four nautical miles to the southeast. In the dawn the thirteen kilometer island was low and gray on the horizon. On the first day, fifty tortoises were taken to the old site. Now it has been a hike of over an hour to reach this spot. They need a moment to recover.

But not long. Soon the tiny creatures, some no bigger than twenty centimeters, the minimum size allowed to leave the safety of the pen, raise their heads, extend their legs, and, with a remarkable confidence,

At dawn Howard Snell repacks the tortoises into sacks for their journey "up country".

set off through the dry stems of the wind — blown herbs. The years that Fausto has dedicated to their care are cast, with the tortoises, to their fate amongst the rocky soil, the cactus, and the breezes of this remote place

Perhaps there is a feeling of parting in all the men. Small flowers are gathered and left by the remaining tortoises. But it is not a gloomy gesture of parting, more a pleasant good luck, for at the old site there is now evidence that the original repatriates are now breeding and island-born hatchlings have already been found. With another seventeen tortoises, the program will celebrate the *one thousandth* tortoise to be repatriated to this island. It's a magnificent achievement.

Yet this work must continue if an ecologically viable population is to establish itself as soon as possible. It is now considered that about four thousand grown animals, with a sex ratio skewed 2:1 in favor of females, may be required to restore the old relationships that existed before the arrival of man. The cactus forests, the predation by hawks on the hatchlings, and the tortoises' ability to survive the harsh changes in climate are some of the factors that must be taken into account.

Station and Park personnel brave the surf to land at dawn on the coral sand beach. In the dinghy is a precious load of 100 tortoises.

A NOTE OF CAUTION

Tortoise country - an ecosystem that has evolved over millennia between herbivorous reptiles and plants...

...even including the Darwin's finches that clean tortoises of their parasites.

*H*owever, survival may not be easy. The whalers, in taking the tortoises, changed the ecosystem of the island. The plant species started growing to a new rhythm without the herbivores, perhaps not so suitable for the giant tortoises. The introduced goats, now long gone, also changed the face of the island. Endemic hawks still quarter the hills and valleys and will eat the hatchlings if given a chance. The Tortoise Breeding Program does not only seek to raise tortoises, but has a much wider vision. It is no less than to restore an ecosystem that existed before man's fateful tread fell on the white sands of Gardner Beach. It will not be in our generation. Maybe it will not be for ten human generations that the island of Española will return to its old ways. But the fact is that it is on its way.

In those years ahead, there will be shady cactus trees. There will be tortoises roaming through the old volcanic hills. The nesting areas will be busy places with female tortoises coming and going. Maybe a tortoise or two will be seen down on the beach, where the green sea turtle trudges ashore to make her nest. Above all the silence of today's spring will be filled with the grunting bellow of the male tortoise's breeding. People will look back and say that the Tortoise Breeding Program did a great job.

Yet it is important to realize that other islands and other populations are not so well off. That the risks of altered ecosystems, which include the introduction of animals, the hunger of man himself, and the difficulty of restoring them, threaten the future of tortoises elsewhere in the Archipelago. The success of breeding the Española race shows that a population can be brought back from the brink of extinction, yet, should their home island be in an unfit condition for them to reproduce and survive on, we gain little. We can grow tortoises but it is obviously preferable not to arrive at the point of having to do so. It is imperative that surviving, reproductively viable populations, living in natural habitats, are given every protection that they need to avoid the necessity of rebuilding both a tortoise population and an ecosystem.

This is emphasized by the critical situation on Alcedo. Alcedo, the central massive shield volcano on the island of Isabela, is the home to the single largest population of tortoises in Galapagos. Its upper reaches are dominated by the ramparts of the base of the volcanic shield, which seemed to protect it from the outside world. The flanks are enormous, wild, and largely untrod by man. Unknown to conservationists, goats were steadily invading this tortoise stronghold. In the 1990s their population exploded over the steep border of the central caldera. A couple of years later, the natural vegetation was becoming severely damaged in the critical southeast rim area, where the tortoises seek water in the dry season when the moist winds blow in from the southeast. Erosion began to cause gullies and landslides, changing, perhaps for ever, the ancient pathways which safely carried the giant tortoises up and down the steep walls. The tortoises are still there but their world is changing around them. An emergency campaign has been started to save the ecosystem of the volcano and, at the same time, to save the largest and most original giant tortoise population that exists today. The past history of the islands insists that this huge effort must succeed in restoring the natural balance of yesterday before it is necessary to consider a captive breeding program, for, as we now know, from that point, it is a very, very long haul upward to gain ground.

Such a program, unfortunately, is already the case for southern Isabela, where a complex of shell shapes, a massive destruction of tortoises in the twentieth

A tortoise grazing on the rim of Alcedo Volcano
before the arrival of feral goats in **1991**.

and the effect of the goats browsing. **1995**.

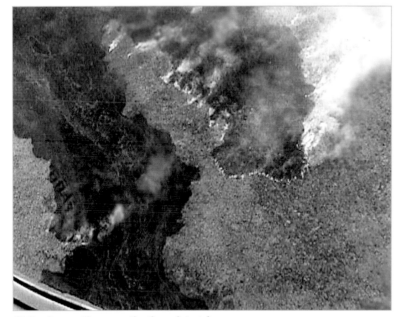

Molten lava cutting a swathe through tortoise
country on Cerro Azul (southern Isabela) in 1998.

A tortoise, scalded by lava in the 1998 eruption of Cerro Azul,
slowly recuperates in the breeding center.

century, which left the populations fragmented and vulnerable, and natural events have made the conservation of these races extremely difficult. Add to this the introduction of pigs, dogs, and even *Solenopsis* fire ants, which are capable of killing the hatchlings, plus the continued slaughter by humans, and the situation becomes extremely serious.

The one factor for which man can be totally free of blame are the unpredictable volcanoes themselves. It is surely true that the tortoises have always lived with the fire of these mountains, especially in the youthful western islands. In 1998, a flank eruption on the southeast side of Cerro Azul

In 1998 a lava flow threatened the rare *aplastado* tortoises of Cerro Azul (southern Isabela). With the aid of a military helicopter, a breeding sample of adults was whisked away to the breeding center at Villamil.

broke out and poured lavas over the surrounding woodland. Moving at a rate of kilometers per day, the river of lava hit the bank of an older flow, which in itself had almost separated the tortoises' access between Cerro Azul and its neighboring volcano, Sierra Negra, and ran toward the sea to the south. Dammed at this point, the flow higher up took a new route to the south.

Trees, torched by the heat, were crushed by the indomitable wall of advancing rock. With uncanny precision, the flow headed toward the nesting area of a rare type of tortoise, known as the *aplastados* (flattened ones) for the low, long carapace shape. Finally a helicopter arrived, requested by the National Park Service and sent by the Ecuadorian military from the mainland. This enabled a group of animals to be whisked out of the way of the impending danger. Where to take them?

The work of the Charles Darwin Research Station and The Galapagos Park Service will secure a future for the beleaguered tortoises of Southern Isabela. The breeding center is operated by the Park Service under the leadership of Juan Chávez (extreme left).

Of the known seventy-three *aplastado* tortoise seventeen live in the breeding center at Villamil. Although many of these have been in captivity for only a few months they have settled down well and show every sign of breeding in the near future. Their natural habitat is on the rough flanks of the volcano Cerro Azul. Their nests are threatened by feral pigs. Their young by introduced ants. Their very lives by hungry men. To cap it all, nature's lava flows threatened to eliminate their nesting grounds in 1998.

Luckily, the Park Service, working hand in glove with the Research Station, had already taken the precaution of building a new breeding center just outside the village of Villamil under the south slope of Sierra Negra. Already the incubators were humming, heating eggs from other rare local populations. The pens were ready. Now there is a small, yet serviceable, population of the *aplastados* ready to perform the same miracle that saved the tortoises of Española from extinction. It is a humbling sight to visit the breeding centers, which are open to the public. Don't pass by without considering that the ancestors of these animals were once kings in Galapagos, their numbers so large that they amazed the early travelers. That in a few short centuries man has reduced many of the populations to a frighteningly low level, some to extinction. The breeding centers are the least we can do to redeem man's actions. Without them we would lose more. With them it is possible for the giant tortoise to survive — and prosper.

A tortoise rest in the shady pens of the breeding center.

Five of the six known Cerro Paloma tortoises.

In the next pen is the remnant of the Cerro Paloma population. There may not be more than ten left and six of them are here in the breeding center. At last, after a frustrating wait of four years, Raquel, one of the two females, constructed two nests from which have emerged nineteen hatchlings. Anxious eyes are on Aflorita, the other female. The population can be saved from extinction but it will require great effort to restore the ecosystem, and, as important, to persuade the people that it is more profitable to preserve the tortoises that eat them!

Raquel an Aflorita. Two females on which the future of the Cerro Paloma population rests.

Two of Raquel's offspring.

Each major volcano of Isabela has a unique population of tortoises. That of Sierra Negra, which once spread over the southern face of the volcano, have been virtually annihilated in this century. From Cerro Paloma there are six known individuals. Two of which are females.

REVELATIONS

Scientists have pondered for many years over the origin of the various shell shapes.
It is now believed that the differences are due to adaptation to environmental
conditions through minor genetic changes.

*T*here can be absolutely no doubt that the saving of the giant tortoises of Galapagos has been worthwhile for its own sake, yet the mere existence of these extraordinary reptiles on remote oceanic islands must promote a whole series of questions that need to be answered to still our curiosity. Nowhere on the planet can be found the remarkable variety of gracefully curving shell shapes except here in the islands. Some are enormous and domed in form, whilst others are smaller with the anterior edge of the carapace arching skyward. These are the saddlebacks.

Why are they different yet fundamentally similar? Why are the saddlebacks unique to Galapagos amongst all known tortoises anywhere in the world? Are all the saddlebacks related somehow? And perhaps the most profound question: Where did they come from?

These uncertainties have dogged investigators for many decades, even centuries. In the early years of scientific study it was certainly the doubts about their relationships that urged that samples from as many populations as possible should be collected and, in later times, that the populations themselves should be saved from extinction.

As far back as 1812, Capitan David Porter, dogging the British whalers in the US Navy frigate *Essex*, observed that the various islands had differently shaped tortoises on them. This was also pointed out to Charles Darwin by the vice-consul Mr. Lawson, when the *Beagle* visited the islands in 1835. Thereafter the scientists got to work on them. This began a series of debates and arguments over their classification that have, to some extent, continued to this day. But that is a matter of names. All agreed that the tortoises were different enough to be separated on a taxonomic basis. Whether they were species, subspecies, or races was another thing. Another point of general agreement was that they seemed to belong to a group of tortoises that occur, or had occurred, around the world. This group is known today as *Geochelone*, the Land Turtles. They've been around for the last thirty million years.

In the nineteenth and for the first half of the twentieth century, the world of science had little more to work on than geography, the fossil record, and the morphology (size, shape, and form) of the animals. Some of these specialists were brilliant workers, exceptionally keen observers, and meticulous in their studies. Often their work on evolutionary relationships stands up even against the most modern techniques.

One such man was John Van Denburgh, a herpetologist working for the California Academy of Sciences. He based his studies on the 256 specimens gathered in 1905-06. He recognized the possible presence of fifteen species, but refrained from naming two because of the lack of specimens. Five of these species were found on the five major shield volcanoes of Isabela. This detailed division is fundamentally recognized today, although the "species" are now considered "races" or "subspecies." Also a taxonomic recommendation considers that the much loved species name *elephantopus* be changed to *nigra*.

About the time the tortoise breeding program began, a revolution in biology was taking place. One of life's deepest secrets, that had eluded man for centuries, was finally being revealed. It was the genetic code, without which life does not exist. As scientists took apart the chromosomes, they found the unique genes. As they took apart the genes, they found the code, composed of endless combinations of nucleotides, of which there are only four types in the massive molecules of nucleic acid, DNA. The nucleotides code for amino acids, which are the building blocks of proteinaceous enzymes. A comparison between the sequences of the amino acid codes from different organisms, the similarity of genes and their placement on the chromosomes, and the chromosomes themselves are all evidence of evolutionary connections. The more similar the patterns are from individual to individual, population to population, species to species, the more closely related these plants or animals are.

Could this novel approach be applied to the tortoises? Could this solve the riddle of the saddlebacks?

Meanwhile the morphology of the tortoises still had something to say. Tom Fritts made careful observations of wild animals and those in captivity. He also compared the islands from which they came. He measured the shells. The results revealed that all were remarkably similar and that the difference in shell shape was in fact a change in growth rate in the vertical plane. It did not need to involve complex genetic alterations, but simple modifications of those in existence. He also established, however, that it was a genetic change and not just a change caused by the environment on certain islands. This he was able to elucidate, because there were tortoises growing up at the Station of both types. Their shell shapes changed even though they were growing up in the same environment.

The conclusion of his studies was that saddlebacks were able to develop in the Galapagos, because there were no large native predators which could attack the vulnerable body where the shell rises at the front. Normally continental tortoises have a low front to the shell as a protection. The saddlebacks occur on low, arid islands, where a small body size could fit into the limited shade and be less demanding both of food and water. Their relatively longer necks and legs made the limited vegetation available to them. Also, since male tortoises dominate each other by trying to raise their heads higher than their opponents, there may be some adaptive advantage in the upturned shell. The strong competition for food may also have caused the animals to disperse widely on an island where food was scarce.

Delving deeper, Tom Fritts found that it wasn't clear cut. Some populations were more or less saddlebacks, others more or less domed. Correlating this with the island environment where they were found seemed to suggest that the tortoises, in their dispersal through the islands, adapted to the local conditions. The assumption is that the originals, which came from mainland South America, were domed. Wet islands, which generally are the larger and higher ones, favored the enormous domed races with their ability to maintain warmth in the cooler, higher environments. Dry islands favored the saddleback. But the curious thing was that this process seemed to have happened a number of times, since the saddlebacks were scattered throughout the Archipelago, interspersed with domed ones. Perhaps in truth domes and saddlebacks were not different lineages but modified forms of the same one. What did the science of genetics say about this?

Ronald Marlow and James Patton were the first in the field. They made a study of enzymes extracted from blood samples and published their results in 1981. This involved seven of the eleven extant races. The purposes of the study were to try to understand the evolutionary history of the tortoises and also to see whether it was possible to identify individuals, for, on the one hand, there were many tortoises scattered throughout the world which might supply vital new blood to a Galapagos population with very low numbers, and, on the other, there were over sixty tortoises at the Station, those received from the local inhabitants, which could not be used for breeding since their origin was unknown.

The extracted enzymes, from twenty gene positions, were compared from over two hundred tortoises from Galapagos and the mainland of South America. The comparison is made by exposing the enzymes, which are placed in a starch gel, to an electric current. Dependent upon the charge in the molecules of the enzyme, they migrate at different speeds across the gel. Very similar animals will display similar movements. The results were disappointing in that no definitive markers could be found to identify individuals with a sufficient degree of confidence, nor could an ancient continental relative be identified. But several findings were of great interest and have been substantiated. Although all the races are extremely similar, there did appear to be groupings, but these were not related to shell shape. For instance, they found that the Pinzon tortoises (saddlebacks) were more closely related to those of Santa Cruz (domed) than those of Pinta (saddlebacks). Like Tom Fritts, these scientists could not find a justification for separating saddlebacks and domes. The most distinctive tortoises, genetically, were found on San Cristobal. The samples from more westerly races indicated a closer relationship. This suggests that the islands were colonized from the east to the west. The extreme similarity of all the races indicates that there was probably only one unique arrival of tortoises from the mainland. We must marvel that such a thing was possible, for tortoises can float in the sea, but their swimming ability does not even warrant them a starting place!

So there still existed the doubt as to who is who.

In the 1980s and 1990s, two new studies were undertaken with the same objectives as those of Ronald Marlow and James Patton. By now the techniques had gone a long way beyond the study of the products of genes. Scientists were now looking at the sequence of nucleotides, the very code itself. This was a huge improvement over the old system, for the coding of enzymes is not that simple. Sometimes the codes partially overlap one another and therefore the production of certain proteins may not reveal all the possibilities of the code. If it is possible to examine the actual nucleotide sequences, it will reveal patterns that are independent of the complexity of the enzymes they produce and may, through comparisons, reveal clues as to the real relationship between populations of tortoises. Changes also occur in what appear to be redundant sections of the code. These are often long sections of short repetitions of nucleotides. These probably undergo changes (mutations) which have little consequence for the animal (non-adaptive) and may come to represent specific forms within a population. Buoyancy tests are capable of separating these areas, since they have a different density to the main body of the DNA molecule. Because they stand apart from the main functioning section of the DNA, like moons from a planet, the test is termed satellite DNA.

Because of its shorter code, extra-nuclear DNA is also studied. This is found in sub-cellular structures, and, in animals is called mitochondrial DNA (mtDNA). They are the powerhouses of animals and are only transmitted by the mother. There are other advantages. The entire genome of mtDNA is known for a diverse number of species and it exhibits relatively rapid sequence evolution. Although these procedures may sound clear cut, they are not! There is always background noise, like static on a radio, and a certain lack of resolution. In general the techniques provide an invaluable tool to evolutionary biologists, but in the case of some tortoise races that are very closely related, the results are not conclusive.

What do they reveal?

In the first place, the work by Ed Louis and that of an international team lead by Jeff Powell, whose work still continues, supports the earlier studies. Working on specific genes, and utilizing hundreds of nucleotide pairs (a nucleotide links to another nucleotide in an entirely predictable way), all the studies agree that the tortoises spread from east to west. All studies agree that the saddlebacks and domed shell shapes have evolved on separate occasions independent of direct genetic lineage. In the later study these later studies, there is an indication that the tortoises of Santiago (intermediate saddleback/dome) are most closely related to those of the northernmost volcano on Isabela, Wolf (saddleback). The work of Jeff Powell's team also shows that the tortoises of Isabela appear to be divided in two groups, suggesting that they arrived there from different islands, perhaps at different times.

Ed Louis was unable to define the races of southern Isabela, which are a curious mixture of shell shapes. In fact the tortoises of mid and southern Isabela are so closely related that they probably represent the latest dispersal of the giants. Moreover it is possible that the dispersal was aided by the ice ages, which lowered the level of the ocean by a hundred meters or so, thus reducing the distance between the islands.

The time estimates are another offshoot of genetic and DNA studies. They are based on the assumption of a molecular clock. The hypothesis is that many changes that occur in the genetic code through mutations are not actively selected for or against. In other words, they are adaptively neutral and do not affect the "fitness" of the organism to survive and reproduce. These changes may accumulate at an average rate over time and reflect the relatedness of groups of animals or plants. From this, actual times of divergence of groups of animals are determined within limits, which are usually quite wide, for doubts exist as to the rates for accumulative change in the genetic code.

But some waves have been thrown up. It all relates to the Española tortoises, whose home is in the extreme southeast of the Archipelago and which display a distinctive genetic pattern. Ed Louis revealed that their genetic signature has been found in some of the tortoises from the western slope of Wolf Volcano, at Bankís Bay (northern Isabela), but not amongst those found on the north slope. How did it get there? Were tortoises introduced there by whalers? By local fishermen? What about those dozens of tortoises thrown into the sea from the decks of the Georgiana and the Policy by anxious British whalers, on the approach of the US warship Essex in 1813? This took place off the north coast of Isabela. Could they have drifted up to the shore, borne on the capricious currents? Did some boat dump the smaller tortoises gathered at Española, finding bigger ones at Bankís Bay? Or was it, after all, a natural event? On the present evidence, the tortoises moved through the Archipelago, in their colonization, with a remarkable facility. Certainly the oceanic currents go that way in a general sense, i.e., from southeast to northwest.

Then there's Lonesome George, the last known survivor from Pinta. He also shows a closer genetic link to Española tortoises than any other race. Was he an exception to the general population on Pinta?. This perhaps we will never know. It has even been mentioned that perhaps all the tortoises on Pinta were descended from some that were introduced by man. This seems very unlikely since it is known that a minimum of over four hundred and fifty were removed by whalers, indicating that there was a substantial population on the island at the end of the 18th century. It seems that Pinta tortoises were indeed a direct line from those of Española, a trick of the pervasive oceanic currents which carried tortoises from one end of the archipelago to the other without leaving them, or a gravid female, on any of the intervening islands! Perhaps George is longing for his southern island mate.

These questions will not be resolved easily. More material from Pinta will be searched for in the museums of the world. Even a piece of thin tortoise shell from some long dead specimen can give genetic clues. These conclusions, whilst initially casting doubts as to the purity of some of the races, are providing hard evidence as to the true relationships between the populations, however they became that way.

Finally, Ed Louis is not convinced that his data are sufficiently clear to act as a definitive way to place every individual into a specific race, particularly those of southern Isabela. The ecologist James Gibbs, who has worked with genetic studies believes that in the near future, given large sample sizes and the latest molecular genetic technology, it should be possible to detect differences, should they exist.

Nevertheless, in a report to the Station, Ed Louis does present locations for fifty- one of the sixty- five unidentified tortoises held there. Possibly the ones he could not identify are hybrids. Interestingly, by far the majority of the captives came from the two populations on Wolf volcano, Isabela, Piedras Blancas (28) and Puerto Bravo (6). The explanation, no doubt, is that both places are anchorages and the tortoises come within a stone's throw of the shore. Unfortunately, none came from Pinta.

And who is the giant tortoises' ancestor? It almost certainly no longer exists and we can only search for the closest living relation. As it is, there are only three species of tortoises living on the whole South American continent ñ and these are all relatively small. The arid ñ dwelling Chaco tortoise (G. chilensis) of Bolivia and Argentina, the relatively large yellow ñ footed tortoise (G. Denticulata), and the moist - loving red footed tortoise (G. Carbonaria). From an ecological point of view the Chaco tortoise would be the choice. This is backed up by genetic studies by Jeff Powell's team, which suggests that the Galapagos giant tortoises are all related within with a maximum divergence of a little over 1%. That they are most closely related to the Chaco tortoise but with a difference of about 8% and to the other mainland tortoises around 12%. Why are they not more closely related to the mainland species? It seems that the giant tortoises that once roamed the South American continent, and most probably closely related to those of Galapagos, finally died out about 100,000 years ago. A tortoise found in Colombia had a shell length of 2.78 meters! That is twice the size of a large one from Galapagos, which measures in at 1.34 meters and weighs over 200 kilograms. To date no material of these giants that can be used in modern genetic studies has been located to verify their relationships. Thus the Galapagos giant tortoises appear to be a relic population of a fauna that was once a common sight on the mainland of South America. They really are a last view of a prehistoric world in the New World.

The evidence of large tortoises on the mainland supports the idea that the giant tortoises of the islands arrived that way. Peter Pritchard, a world expert on tortoises and turtles, believes, if anything, there may have been a tendency to *reduce* size, as demonstrated by the saddlebacks. The question of size is also involved in the extraordinary event that brought the first animals to the islands. Were they swept out to sea by a swirling river engorged by torrential rains? Perhaps the river bank was undercut and trees, tortoises and all, were carried away in a great tangled mass. To survive the journey of at least ten days, a large

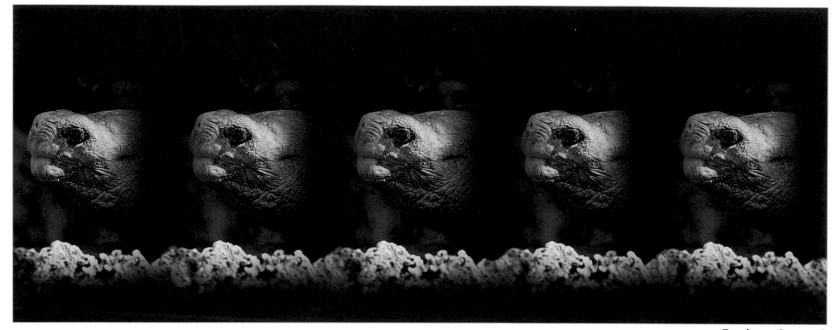

To clone George?

body would be useful, maybe essential. Large fat reserves, a reduction in water loss from a relatively low surface-to-volume ratio, and the ability to keep the head high out of the water, all enhance the chance of completing this incredible journey.

Finally, before we leave the scientific revelations of the last few years, it is relevant to refer to Lonesome George. Is it really the end of the line?

George is, of course, a concern to everybody. He is the unquestionable symbol of all that can go wrong. His island home, Pinta, was ransacked for tortoises by the nineteenth century seaman. Goats were introduced, which destroyed the vegetation, thus totally altering the natural environment. George, alone, the last of his kind, will not breed for unknown reasons.

Is it extinction in 10, 30, or 100 years? For without sex, there will be no offspring.

•The first is that other tortoises still roam the difficult terrain of Pinta. A special project would be needed to mount an exhaustive search.

•The second is to search through the captive tortoises of the world in the hope that Pinta animals still survive.

•Then, in 1997, Dolly, a Scottish sheep, was produced by cloning. The inevitable question arose. If sheep, why not tortoises? Why not George?

The reason for this upsurge of interest in cloning was the method used. Up to that point, and it is noteworthy that frogs were being cloned thirty years ago, the scientific community believed that the donor cells (those to be cloned), with their genetic code, needed to come from a very young embryo. These cells were inserted into a recipient egg, whose genetic material had been removed. Development was fired up by an electric shock, which simulated the meeting of egg and sperm.

What was new, in the case of Dolly, was that the donor cells were taken from the udder, not from an embryo. This meant that perhaps other cells from other tissues might be used in cloning.

This is pertinent to George, for obviously there is no possibility of cells from an embryo, only cells from George himself. Are there cells within a male tortoise that could be induced to develop into a complete copy? With this new breakthrough, perhaps he could be cloned. The cells would have to be placed into empty eggs (empty in the sense that the genetic material had been removed) from another tortoise and placed within a surrogate mother for the eggs to grow. When laid, they could be gathered and incubated. Depending on the temperature, the result might not be a George but a Georgina!

Produce more males and females and a new race is born — with enormous risks that genetic flaws would become embedded in the animals from a lack of genetic variability within the tiny cloned population.

Furthermore, it is still not easy to clone. Only about 1-2% of attempts are successful. It is also very expensive and the results unsure. Thus, for the moment, George remains as a sad reminder of past mistakes. He wanders his corral with other tortoises, two females from Wolf Volcano on northern Isabela, a blue mountain clearly visible from Pinta. The females had been considered the closest genetic relations to George, but he shows little interest in them and no offspring have been forthcoming.

Thus the Galapagos tortoises remain as a unique species, with unique variations, of an enigmatic origin. A rare reminder of bygone days. It is no wonder that they should receive such special conservation efforts or that they have become the symbol of both the Galapagos National Park and the Charles Darwin Foundation.

FURTHER READING

- **Cayot, Linda J., Howard L. Snell, Washington Llerena, and Heidi M. Snell. 1994.** Conservation biology of Galapagos reptiles: Twenty five years of successful research and management. *In* J.B. Murphy, K. Adler, and J.T. Collins, eds., *Captive management and conservation of amphibians and reptiles,* Society for the Study of Amphibians and Reptiles, Ithaca, New York, Contributions to Herpetology 11: 297-305.

- **Fritts, Thomas and Patricia Fritts, eds. 1982.** *Race with extinction: Herpetological notes of J.R. Slevin's journey to the Galapagos 1905-1906.* Herpetological Monograph No. 1. Herpetologists' League, Lawrence, Kansas.

- **MacFarland, Craig and Jan MacFarland. 1972.** Goliaths of the Galapagos. *National Geographic* 142 (5): 632-649.

- **MacFarland, Craig, José Villa, and Basilio Toro. 1974.** The Galapagos giant tortoises *(Geochelone elephantopus)* Part II: Conservation methods. Biological Conservation 6 (3) : 198-212.

- **Louis, Edward, Scott K. Davis, and Jeremy F. Taylor. (undated).** Report on the Galapagos Tortoises held at the CDRS. Located at the library of the Charles Darwin Research Station.

- **Márquez, Cruz, Linda Cayot, and Solanda Rea. In prep.** La crianza de tortugas gigantes en cautiverio: Un manual operativo. Charles Darwin Foundation, Quito.

- **Pritchard, Peter. 1996.** *The Galapagos Tortoise: Nomenclature and survival status.* Chelonian Research Monographs No. 1. Chelonian Research Foundation, Lunenberg, Massachusetts.

- **Slevin, Joseph. 1931.** Log of the schooner " Academy " on a voyage of scientific research to the Galapagos Islands 1905-1906. *Occasiona Papers of the California Academy of Sciences* 17: 1-162.

- **Thornton, Ian. 1971.** *Darwin's Islands: A natural history of the Galapagos.* Natural History Press (Doubleday and Company), New York.

- **Townsend, Charles. 1925.** The Galapagos tortoises in relation to the whaling industry. *Zoologica* 4 (3): 55-135.

- **Van Denburgh, John. 1914.** Expedition of the California Academy of Sciences to the Galapagos Islands 1905-1906. X. The gigantic land tortoises of the Galapagos Archipelago. *Proceedings of the California Academy of Sciences,* Fourth Series 2: 203-374.